HIGHLAND GEOLOGY TRAIL

By JOHN L. ROBERTS

TABLE OF CONTENTS

Published by Strathtongue Press, Tongue by Lairg, Sutherland IV27 4XR

CODE OF CONDUCT IN THE FIELD

Geologising in the field is not without its physical dangers, like any outdoor activity. The hazards can be reduced by wearing suitable clothing and sensible footwear, preferrably a pair of good boots. A compass and map should always be carried, together with food for any emergency. Keep away from dangerous cliffs, and beware of incoming tides. Always obey the Country Code: do not leave gates open; never climb over dry stone walls; do not trample crops; do not disturb farm animals; and do not leave any litter. Although trepass is not a criminal offence in Scotland, there is no right of access to the countryside. Permission should always be asked as appropriate from landowners, their agents or tenants. Respect any sporting interests in the land.

NEVER HAMMER ROCK EXPOSURES WHICH SHOW ANY FEATURES OF GEOLOGICAL INTEREST. THIS APPLIES IN PARTICULAR TO OUTCROPS AFFECTED BY WEATHERING

The use of geological hammers should be restricted in the interests of conservation. Much can be seen by using a hand lens on weathered surfaces, without the need for hammering. If absolutely necessary to break open fresh rock, only hammer loose specimens or fallen blocks. Keep the collecting of rock, mineral and fossil specimens to an absolute minimum.

MACMILLAN FIELD GUIDE TO GEOLOGICAL STRUCTURES

The initials **MFG** and a number refer to the localities where the corresponding photographs were taken for this field guide. It also provides a complete description of all the geological features likely to be seen in the field.

ISBN 0 9515866 0 2

Typeset using Locoscript 2 printed on Amstrad 9512.

ORDNANCE SURVEY MAPS

No serious exploration of the Scottish Highlands can be undertaken without the use of topographic maps. The Landranger Maps published on a scale of 1:50,000 by the Ordnance Survey are the best available. They allow the National Grid System to be used to maximum advantage. However, the Ordnance Survey also publishes Atlases on scales of 1:100,000 and 1:250,000, covering much more ground at much less cost, which provide a less satisfactory alternative.

GEOLOGICAL SURVEY MAPS

The most useful geological map for the visitor is the Ten Miles to One Inch Geological Map of Great Britain (Solid Geology). Sheet One covers the Scottish Highlands. Other geological maps are available at 1:250,000 and 1:50,000.

LOCAL FIELD-GUIDES

Lewisian and Torridonian rocks of North-West Scotland. Geologists' Association Guide (Number 21).

Excursion Guide to the Assynt District of Scotland. Published by the Edinburgh Geological Society.

Excursion Guide to the Geology of the Isle of Skye. Published by the Geological Society of Glasgow.

Ardnamurchan: a Guide to Geological Excursions. Published by the Edinburgh Geological Society.

Guide to the Moine Geology of the Scottish Highlands. Published by Scottish Academic Press, Edinburgh.

REGIONAL GEOLOGY (BRITISH GEOLOGICAL SURVEY)

Northern Highlands of Scotland; Grampian Highlands of Scotland; Tertiary Volcanic Districts of Scotland. HMSO.

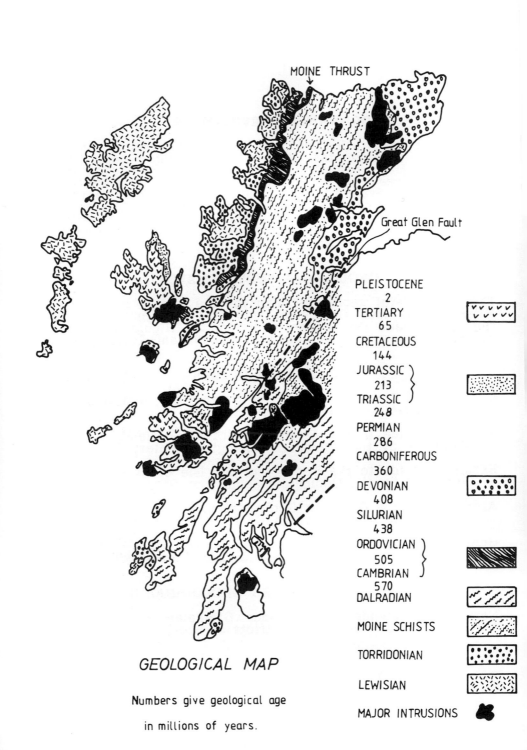

MOINE THRUST

Great Glen Fault

PLEISTOCENE
2
TERTIARY
65
CRETACEOUS
144
JURASSIC ⎫
213 ⎬
TRIASSIC ⎭
248
PERMIAN
286
CARBONIFEROUS
360
DEVONIAN
408
SILURIAN
438
ORDOVICIAN ⎫
505 ⎬
CAMBRIAN ⎭
570
DALRADIAN

MOINE SCHISTS

TORRIDONIAN

LEWISIAN

MAJOR INTRUSIONS

GEOLOGICAL MAP

Numbers give geological age

in millions of years.

HIGHLAND GEOLOGY TRAIL

NATURE OF THE GEOLOGICAL RECORD.

Geology is essentially a historical science, much concerned with the dating of rocks. Their age can be determined by using a timescale constructed from the nature of the geological record itself. It was first recognised at the start of the 19th century that the age of sedimentary rocks could be established by studying the fossils they contain. Indeed, it was the sudden appearance of hard-bodied animals some 570 million years ago that allowed geologists to divide geological time into two distinct eras. The shells or other hard parts of these animals could then be preserved as fossils. This occurred at the start of Cambrian times. The whole of geological time from the origin of the Earth, some 4600 million years ago, up to this time is therefore known as the Precambrian.

The Precambrian represents nearly seven-eighths of geological time, as it lasted for nearly 4000 million years. There are few fossils preserved in rocks of Precambrian age, apart from very small organisms such as plant spores and the like, along with the impressions of soft-bodied animals. This means the Precambrian record can only be divided up in a much cruder fashion than is possible once Cambrian times are reached.

It was the evolution of hard-bodied animals at the start of Cambrian times which allowed a detailed timescale to be devised for the more recent events in the geological history of the Earth. The subsequent evolution of particular species during the course of this history, coupled with their occasional extinction, means that rocks can be dated geologically by studying the fossils found within them. The nature of this record is such that this latter part of geological time can be divided up into a number of different periods. Each is given a name, and taken together, these various periods of geological time then constitute what is known as the geological timescale, as shown in the legend accompanying the geological map.

All rocks are formed in response to physical processes, acting at a particular time during the course of geological history, and this is an equally important aspect of the geological record. In fact, Geology divides rocks into three distinct categories: sedimentary, igneous and metamorphic, according to their mode of origin.

Sedimentary rocks are derived from the weathering and erosion of pre-existing rocks. This produces sedimentary

1

SEDIMENTARY ROCKS

detritus, chiefly mineral grains and rock fragments, which is mostly carried across the Earth's surface by water, only to accumulate away from its source as flat-lying layers of sedimentary rock. **Igneous rocks** are formed wherever molten lava, or its underground equivalent, cools and solidifies. If this occurs very rapidly, molten lava may be quenched so that it forms a glassy rock, lacking any crystalline structure. More commonly, minerals start to crystallise out from such a melt, and when this crystallisation is complete, a solid rock is formed. **Metamorphic rocks** are formed wherever pre-existing rocks are so altered in response to extremes of temperature and pressure that they take on an entirely different character. These changes occur in the solid rock as a result of chemical reactions between its original minerals, causing these minerals to recrystallise, or allowing new minerals to grow in their place.

SEDIMENTARY ROCKS.

Sedimentary rocks are composed of material that is ultimately derived from the weathering and erosion of pre-existing rocks. They are therefore a major repository of geological history, reflecting the nature of the environmental conditions under which they were once laid down as distinct layers upon the Earth's surface. These layers are known as **sedimentary beds,** and it is thought that they were very close to the horizontal at the time of their deposition. Although usually only a few feet thick, sedimentary beds can often be traced horizontally for considerable distances.

Sedimentary rocks therefore display a layered structure known as **bedding** or **stratification.** Each bed of sedimentary rock is always laid down on top of rocks already deposited, so that any sedimentary sequence is always arranged chronologically in an orderly manner: the oldest beds occur at its base, passing upwards into ever younger horizons towards its top. This is known as the **Principle of Superposition.** It allows sedimentary rocks to be dated with respect to one another.

Sedimentary beds are separated from one another by **bedding-planes,** along which the rock will usually split apart. Such beds can usually be distinguished in the field by differences in grain-size, texture, colour, hardness and composition. The bedding is often picked out by weathering and erosion, so that it can be recognised in virtually every exposure of sedimentary rock. Indeed, it is the first feature to look for when out geologising in the field.

CONGLOMERATES AND BRECCIAS. How sedimentary rocks are derived from the weathering and erosion of pre-existing rocks is particularly clear in the case of conglomerates and breccias. These rocks are just accumulations of rock fragments, which must have been derived from an area of older rocks, often set in a much finer-grained matrix. **Conglomerates** consist of pebbles and boulders, which have probably been transported for some distance, to judge by their well-rounded nature. **Breccias** consist of angular rock fragments without any rounding of their corners, obviously derived from nearby.

SHALES AND MUDSTONES. Weathering and erosion may also break down the rocks exposed on land into much smaller particles, so providing another source of sedimentary material. The chemical breakdown of the minerals forming these rocks often leads to the formation of clay particles, microscopic in size, while leaving quartz and other relatively resistant minerals unaffected. Carried away from their source by running water, these particles are transported far and wide until they eventually settle out of suspension in still water, most usually as mud on the sea-floor. Such deposits harden into shale and mudstone. **Shales** are very fine-grained sedimentary rocks composed of clay minerals, which split easily along the bedding into very thin leaves. Except that **mudstones** do not split so easily along the bedding, they are rocks otherwise similar to shales. Both rock-types are susceptible to further weathering and erosion, so that they are often not well-exposed at the surface.

SANDSTONES, ARKOSES AND GREYWACKES. The mineral grains which escape the effects of chemical breakdown can also be carried away from their source by running water. However, this detrital material is much coarser in grain than clay or mud, so that it is eventually deposited as sand. **Sandstone** is formed wherever these mineral grains become compacted and cemented together to form a solid rock. Most sandstones consist of quartz grains, since this mineral is particularly resistant to chemical weathering. However, the physical breakdown of rocks like granite and gneiss under conditions of very rapid erosion often leads to the presence of much feldspar as well as quartz in the rock, which is then known as an **arkose.** Although it is not common in the Scottish Highlands, another type of sandstone consists of a wide variety of

3

rock fragments and mineral grains, set in a finer-grained matrix rich in clay minerals. It is called a **greywacke.**

The sedimentary grains in a sandstone can often be seen using a hand lens of moderate magnification on a weathered surface, particularly if they are cemented together by calcite, dolomite or hydrous iron oxides. However, where the grains are quartz, cemented together by the same mineral, they become much less conspicuous, unless some feldspar is also present in the rock. If this forms a very hard rock, which typically breaks across the mineral grains, it is known as a **quartzite.** Such rocks are usually white or grey in colour.

CROSS-BEDDING AND GRADED-BEDDING. Sandstones often display two quite distinct types of sedimentary structure. Firstly, **cross-bedding** is a common feature of sandstones laid down in relatively shallow water. It occurs wherever the internal bedding-planes within a sedimentary bed are inclined at an angle to the upper or lower contacts of the bed itself. Often, these internal bedding-planes are curved so that they are truncated by erosion along the upper contact, while they become flat-lying as they are traced towards the lower contact. This means that cross-bedding can be used to tell if the sedimentary beds are right-way-up or upside down. Secondly, **graded-bedding** occurs wherever the grain-size decreases towards the top of a sedimentary bed, away from its base. This is rather more typical of sandstones like greywackes, which were deposited in relatively deep water. Like cross-bedding, graded-bedding can be used to determine if the sedimentary beds are right-way-up or upside down.

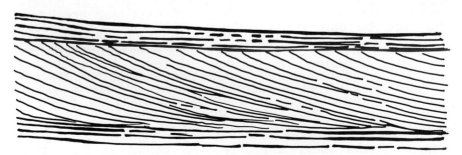

Figure 1. Cross-bedding.

4

LIMESTONES AND DOLOMITES. Chemical weathering also produces material in solution, which eventually finds its way into the oceans. There, concentrated by evaporation, it forms salt water. These salts, dissolved in sea-water, can be precipitated directly as a result of further evaporation, so forming various types of salt deposit, or they can be abstracted by living organisms to form their hard parts. When these animals die, their hard parts may then accumulate as sedimentary deposits on the sea-floor.

Limestones in particular are formed by a combination of these processes, being partly chemical precipitates and partly the accumulation of organic remains. They are calcareous rocks rich in calcium carbonate, which occurs in the form of calcite, and not surprisingly, they often have fossils preserved within them. Once deposited, limestones may be altered chemically by brines rich in dissolved salts to form **dolomite.** This rock is largely composed by the mineral also known as dolomite, which is a carbonate of magnesium as well as calcium. Calcite and dolomite are easily scratched with a knife, and this serves to distinguish these minerals from the quartz in sandstones.

Limestones and dolomites are rocks which are rather easily dissolved away by rain water, carrying carbon dioxide in solution. This produces a landscape typical of limestone, with its flat-lying outcrops occurring in the form of limestone pavements. Where rain-water runs down any steep faces on limestone, it often dissolves away the rock to make an intricately fretted surface with very sharp edges. Typically, limestone makes fertile ground, covered with grass, unlike sandstone where often only heather and bracken will grow.

EVIDENCE FOR EARTH-MOVEMENTS.

The nature of the geological record suggests that movements of the Earth's crust have occurred almost continuously during the course of geological time. Apart from limestones and dolomites, sedimentary rocks can only be deposited if there is a suitable source of detrital material. However, this supply can only be maintained if uplift exposes ever more rock to weathering and erosion within the source area. Likewise, there is only space for the long-continued accumulation of sedimentary rocks if the Earth's crust continues to subside, so forming a sedimentary basin. Such movements of uplift and subsidence also provide a slope down which the sedimentary detritus can be moved under the influence of gravity away from its source into such a sedimentary basin.

There is more direct evidence that earth-movements have affected sedimentary rocks after their deposition. It is thought that nearly all sedimentary rocks were deposited very close to the horizontal. However, it is frequently found that earth-movements have tilted the bedding away from this position, so that the sedimentary beds are now found, lying at an angle to the horizontal. This can be measured in the field, using a compass and clinometer. The **compass** is used to measure the trend of an horizontal line drawn across a bedding plane. This gives the **strike** of the bedding as a bearing from true north. The clinometer is then used to measure the angle made by the bedding plane to the horizontal. This gives the **dip** of the bedding plane. It has a maximum value in a direction at right angles to the strike, running straight down the bedding plane.

FOLDING AND FAULTING. The folding of sedimentary rocks is another result of earth-movements. Anticlines and synclines are then formed as the bedding is bent into waves, forming arches and troughs in the rock. **Anticlines** (or up-folds) are usually separated from one another by **synclines** (or down-folds). The folding of sedimentary rocks is commonly the reason why the bedding is no longer close to the horizontal. It dips away from anticlines, towards the intervening synclines, passing through the horizontal across the crests and troughs of these folds.

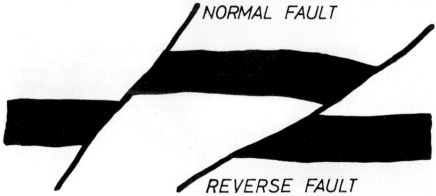

Figure 2. Normal and Reverse Faults.

ANGULAR UNCONFORMITIES

Metamorphic rocks frequently show very intense folding, so that it is not just a feature of sedimentary rocks. Often, this occurs in response to repeated phases of deformation, so that the folds in metamorphic rocks may belong to more than one generation.

Earth-movements can also cause rocks to fracture and break, forming joints and faults. **Joints** are seen in virtually every exposure, forming closely-spaced fractures in the rock, across which no movement can be detected. They often occur in a very regular manner, forming one or more sets of parallel fractures, spaced at a regular interval, particularly in sedimentary rocks. **Faults** differ from joints in that actual movement has occurred along the fracture. This results in a fault-plane, across which the rocks on either side have moved past one another, parallel to the fracture itself.

If the movements occur up or down a fault-plane, the rocks on one side are thrown up while the rocks on the other side are thrown down. A **normal fault** then dips in the direction of its downthrow, often at a steep angle. The opposite relationship is seen in a **reverse fault**, where the overlying rocks have been thrust up the fault-plane, which often dips at rather a shallow angle in the opposite direction. However, it is equally possible for horizontal movements to occur along the strike of the fault-plane. The Great Glen Fault is a good example of such a **strike-slip fault**, which was formed by the rocks of Northern Highlands moving southwest past the rocks of the Grampian Highlands over a distance of some 40 miles.

ANGULAR UNCONFORMITIES.

The folding and faulting of sedimentary rocks is often accompanied by uplift and erosion. This typically produces a surface of erosion, cutting across the bedding of these older rocks, where it dips away from the horizontal. If deposition were then renewed, a younger sequence of flat-lying sediments would be laid down across these older rocks. The resulting structure is known as an **angular unconformity**. It represents a break in deposition, marked by uplift and erosion at a time when earth-movements had also affected the underlying rocks. Its essential feature is the presence of a structural discordance between an older group of rocks, whether sedimentary, igneous or metamorphic, and a younger sequence of flat-lying sediments laid down on top.

7

Figure 3. Angular Unconformity and a Buried Landscape.

Angular unconformities often represent surfaces of erosion that were themselves very close to the horizontal when the overlying rocks were deposited. This often occurs where the sea invades the land, reducing the old land-surface to a flat-lying plane of marine erosion, which then serves as the foundation for the deposition of more sedimentary rocks. If these rocks were laid down as beds very close to the horizontal, as likely to be the case, the bedding of these rocks would then be parallel to the unconformity. However, erosion might not always be able to reduce the surface of unconformity to a horizontal plane before deposition was renewed. This typically occurs where the unconformity represents an ancient landscape, which still preserves a degree of topographic relief. The younger sediments are then often found banked against the older rocks, wedging out against these older rocks along the unconformity itself. Further deposition then results in a buried landscape, which can be exhumed at a later date.

IGNEOUS ROCKS.

Deep within the Earth, temperatures are sufficiently high for melting to occur, at least locally. The molten rock so formed is known as **magma**, and it eventually solidifies to form the **igneous rocks**. If magma escapes towards the surface, it often erupts as lava from volcanoes, cooling down and solidifying as **lava-flows**. They typically erupt

8

one after another, so forming a volcanic sequence in much the same way as sedimentary rocks are deposited one on top of another. However, if the volcanic eruptions are more explosive in nature, the force of these explosions may be sufficient to shatter the walls of the volcanic vent, producing much fragmental material. **Pyroclastic rocks** then accumulate within and around the vent to form **agglomerate** if the fragments are so large that they can easily be seen, or **volcanic ash** or **tuff** if it is much finer in grain-size.

Magma in forcing its way upwards usually encounters colder country-rocks as it rises towards the surface. Often, it cools down and solidifies while it is still at considerable depths within the Earth. This results in what are known as **igneous intrusions.** As they are surrounded on all sides by older rocks, they can be dated as younger than their country-rocks. The heat carried by igneous intrusions often alters and metamorphoses these country-rocks, forming what are known as **metamorphic aureoles.**

Some intrusions of igneous rock occupy vertical fractures which the magma wedged apart as it flowed upwards, so forming a wall-like mass known as a **dyke.** Other intrusions are the result of magma flowing horizontally along the bedding of sedimentary rocks, lifting up its roof to form a sheet-like body known as a **sill.** Both dykes and sills often show **columnar jointing,** where joints are formed at right angles to the surfaces against which the magma cooled. Igneous intrusions also occur as very large masses of igneous rock, known as **batholiths,** which appear to lack any foundation of older rocks at depth.

TEXTURES OF IGNEOUS ROCKS. Wherever lava erupts from volcanoes, it tends to cool down very quickly. In fact, it may just pass into a glassy state, without any crystallisation taking place at all. More usually, however, a fine-grained rock with a crystalline texture is produced. Unless the lava carried up larger crystals from depth, it is not easy to see the individual grains in the rock, even with the aid of a hand-lens. Dykes and sills resemble lava-flows in that they have large areas of cooling surface, lying in contact with their country-rocks, at least in relation to their volume. Such bodies tend to cool down rapidly, so that they usually consist of relatively fine-grained rocks. They often exhibit **chilled margins** against their country-rocks, marked by narrow selvedges of much finer-grained or even glassy rock.

IGNEOUS ROCKS

Batholiths and other deep-seated igneous intrusions invariably cool down very slowly, perhaps taking several million years to reach the temperature of their surroundings. This only allows a relatively small number of largish crystals to grow as the magma solidifies, rather than a multitude of much smaller ones, so producing a coarse-grained rock as a result.

ROCK-FORMING MINERALS. It should first be realised that rocks are made up of different minerals, occurring together as distinct grains in the rock. Apart from calcite and dolomite, which are carbonate minerals, nearly all rocks are composed of silicate minerals, since silicon and oxygen are the two most common chemical elements in the Earth as a whole. These elements combine in various ways with aluminium, sodium, potassium, calcium, iron and magnesium to form a wide variety of silicate minerals, often with very complex compositions.

The most important silicate minerals are known as the **feldspars,** which are complex alumino-silicates of sodium, potassium and calcium. Feldspar occurs as pale pink or whitish grains, often rather massive but showing a good cleavage, which reflects the light in an iridescent fashion. It cannot be scratched with a knife. Igneous rocks containing much feldspar therefore tend to be light in colour, particularly if they are coarse-grained. Where there is not sufficient sodium, potassium or calcium in a rock to combine with silicon and oxygen to form feldspar, silica may be found in the form of **quartz.** This colourless mineral usually has a "glassy" appearance, as it lacks any cleavage. It is slightly harder than feldspar.

The other silicate minerals commonly found in igneous rocks are mostly rich in iron and magnesium. They are often dark in colour, owing to the presence of iron. **Olivine** is a relatively simple silicate of iron and magnesium, often greenish in colour as the name suggests. The **pyroxenes** such as augite are much more complex silicates of calcium, iron and magnesium, often combined with some aluminium. The **amphiboles** are rather similar, except that they are hydrous silicates of calcium, iron and magnesium, often with sodium and aluminium as well. **Hornblende** is a typical amphibole. The **micas** are another group of silicate minerals commonly found in igneous rocks. **Biotite** is a dark mica, rich in magnesium and iron, while **muscovite** is a white mica, rich in aluminium. Mica typically occurs as tabular crystals with a perfect cleavage in one direction.

METAMORPHIC ROCKS

NAMING IGNEOUS ROCKS. Igneous rocks were originally classified according to the amount of silica in the chemical analysis. **Acid rocks** like granite are rich in silica, potash and soda, but poor in iron oxides, magnesia and lime, while **basic rocks** such as gabbro are the reverse, rich in iron oxides, magnesia and lime, but poor in silica, potash and soda.

A great many different types of igneous rock have been recognised over the years. However, granite and gabbro are the two most common rock-types found among the coarse-grained varieties which typically form large intrusive masses. **Granite** is a light-coloured rock composed mostly of potash feldspar, possibly with soda feldspar as well, together with an appreciable amount of quartz. Hornblende and biotite are common as accessory minerals, giving a somewhat speckled appearance to the rock. Granite may also occur as **pegmatite,** which is an extremely coarse-grained rock consisting of quartz and feldspar, together with muscovite in many cases. **Gabbro** is a much darker rock than granite, consisting mostly of calcic feldspar and pyroxene in roughly equal amounts. Olivine is often present in the rock. There is, however, a whole range of igneous rocks, intermediate in composition between granite and gabbro, such as granodiorite, quartz-diorite and diorite. These rocks are often just called granite in the field, all sharing much the same texture.

Coarse-grained igneous rocks have their fine-grained equivalents in the volcanic rocks, typically occurring as lava-flows or dykes and sills, rather than deep-seated intrusions. The fine-grained equivalent of granite is **rhyolite,** which mostly occurs as a pale flow-banded rock. **Andesite** is a much more basic rock, closer in chemical composition to gabbro, often forming a rather dark rock of purple hue. **Basalt** is the fine-grained equivalent of gabbro. It occurs as a very dark or even blackish rock, which weathers easily to form a brownish coating on its surface. **Dolerite** is the intrusive and somewhat coarser-grained equivalent of basalt, often found making up fairly large sills.

METAMORPHIC ROCKS.

Metamorphism occurs wherever solid rocks buried deep within the Earth are altered to such an extent that they take on an entirely different character. They are then known as **metamorphic rocks.** Such changes often occur

METAMORPHIC ROCKS

in response to the influx of heat, carried perhaps by igneous intrusions. This causes the pre-existing minerals in the rock to recrystallise, often forming a coarser-grained rock as a result. Entirely new minerals may also be formed in the solid rock, so that metamorphism often changes both the texture and the mineral composition of the original rock. An aureole of **contact** or **thermal metamorphism** is produced around an igneous intrusion where such changes affect the nearby country-rocks.

However, metamorphism is often much more pervasive in its effects, particularly where very large masses of sedimentary and igneous rocks are caught up in **mountain-building processes** as the result of **earth-movements.** It is often accompanied by intense deformation which completely alters the structural features shown by the metamorphosed rocks, as well as changing their mineral composition. Since these changes typically affect rocks exposed over very wide areas, they come under the heading of **regional metamorphism.**

NAMING METAMORPHIC ROCKS. The nomenclature of metamorphic rocks is relatively simple, since it is based essentially on their textural and structural features, developed in various types of sedimentary and igneous rocks. Sandstones and limestones often just recrystallise to form **quartzites** and **marbles,** without any change in their mineral composition. They are usually coarser in grain than the sandstones and limestones from which they were formed. Such rocks are found in aureoles of contact metamorphism, or as a product of regional metamorphism.

Shales and mudstones are much more susceptible to changes in mineral composition. Contact metamorphism typically converts them into a hard and very splintery rock known as a **hornfels.** This rock is tough and rather fine-grained, often purplish in colour. Any pre-existing structures such as bedding are often obscured or even completely destroyed by the effects of recrystallisation and the growth of new minerals in the rock.

Quite different rocks are produced from shales and mudstones as a result of regional metamorphism. Where deformation affects these rocks at relatively low temperatures, they are converted into **slates.** A slaty cleavage is imposed on the rock, whereby it splits into extremely thin sheets, lying oblique to the bedding. It is produced by recrystallisation of the original clay minerals in the rock so that they all lie parallel to one another. It is often picked out by the weathering. Slates pass into

12

phyllites as the rock becomes slightly coarser in grain, imparting a silky sheen to the cleavage surfaces.

Under conditions of higher temperature, and possibly in response to greater pressures, slates and phyllites pass in their turn into **schists.** These are distinctly crystalline rocks, in which micas like biotite and muscovite all lie roughly parallel to one another, forming what is known as a schistosity. Often, there are other metamorphic minerals present in the rock, such as garnet, so forming **garnetiferous mica-schists.** Igneous rocks like basalt and dolerite may also be converted into **hornblende-schists** or **amphibolites** under similar metamorphic conditions.

Even coarser-grained rocks may be produced in response to regional metamorphism, giving rise to **gneisses** rather than schists. **Gneisses** have a much more even-grained texture than schists, partly owing to the presence of much more feldspar in the rock. They often occur as banded rocks with distinct layers, differing in mineral composition from one another. Gneisses can be formed from a very wide variety of original rocks, in response to the temperatures and pressures which exist at great depths within the Earth's crust. Depending on their composition, they can often be distinguished as acid or basic, according to whether they were formed originally from granite or gabbro. Other gneisses are derived from the metamorphism of sedimentary rocks. All gneisses typically occur as very old rocks, which are often found underlying all the other rocks of a particular region, forming its geological foundations. Such rocks then constitute what is known as a **basement complex.**

Metamorphism usually results in more coarse-grained rocks than originally the case, even if recrystallisation and the growth of new minerals are accompanied by deformation. However, the deformation may be so intense that the original minerals in the rock are broken down into much finer-grained material, particularly where low temperatures do not favour much recrystallisation. The rocks formed as a result are known as **mylonites.** They are extremely fine-grained rocks with a banded or streaky appearance in the field.

HIGHLAND GEOLOGY TRAIL

GEOLOGICAL RECORD IN THE HIGHLANDS.

The Scottish Highlands are underlain by rocks which differ widely in age. Very ancient rocks are found in the Northwest Highlands and Outer Hebrides, where the **Lewisian Gneiss** is exposed over wide areas. It is overlain unconformably by the much younger rocks of the **Torridonian Sandstone,** followed in its turn by a sequence of **Cambro-Ordovician** rocks. All these rocks are separated from the rest of the Scottish Highlands by a great dislocation, known as the **Moine Thrust,** which runs up to 20 miles inland along the western seaboard of the Scottish Highlands. It can be traced from Loch Eriboll and Whiten Head in the north to the Sound of Sleat, between Skye and the mainland in the south, where it passes southwest out to sea. The Moine Thrust marks the western limit to the Caledonian (and earlier) earth-movements, which affected the metamorphic rocks now forming the rest of the Scottish Highlands, towards the end of Silurian times, around 400 million years ago.

These metamorphic rocks are known collectively as the **Highland Schists.** They fall into two distinct groups. The **Moine Schists** are the older rocks, and they have had a very complex history. They are found immediately to the east of the Moine Thrust, forming most of the Northern Highlands to the northwest of the Great Glen, and stretching southeast into the Grampian Highlands as well. Intensely deformed areas of Lewisian Gneiss are also found in the Northern Highlands, entirely surrounded by the Moine Schists. The younger group of metamorphic rocks is known as the **Dalradian Series.** It outcrops over a wide area in the Grampian Highlands, southeast of the Moine Schists. Both Moine and Dalradian rocks are intruded by a great many igneous masses, mostly of granite and related rock-types.

Even younger rocks of Devonian age occur as a sedimentary fringe around both shores of the Moray Firth, where they are found in the guise of the **Old Red Sandstone,** overlain locally by **Permo-Triassic** and **Jurassic** rocks. These Devonian rocks extend into Caithness and the Orkney Islands, while volcanic rocks of roughly the same age are found in the Southwest Highlands, where they form the **Lorne Lavas.**

Finally, the Inner Hebrides were the focus of much igneous activity in Tertiary times. **Intrusive complexes** forming the roots of ancient volcanoes are now exposed on

14

LEWISIAN GNEISS

Skye, Rhum, Mull and Arran, together with Ardnamurchan. **Tertiary lavas** form thick volcanic sequences on Skye and Mull, underlain by Triassic and Jurassic rocks.

LEWISIAN GNEISS.

The oldest rocks found anywhere in the British Isles are formed by the **Lewisian Gneiss,** which is exposed in the far northwest of the Scottish Highlands, together with the islands of the Outer Hebrides. Indeed, there are few rocks quite as old anywhere else in Europe, apart from some very ancient rocks in Finland, and perhaps even older rocks in the Ukraine. Otherwise, Europe is underlain by much younger rocks, belonging to more recent cycles of geological activity, which separate these ancient massifs from one another. We have to look west to find such ancient rocks of a similar character, exposed in Greenland and Labrador. Although the Atlantic Ocean now intervenes, this was not always the case. In fact, the Northwest Highlands of Scotland, lying beyond the Moine Thrust, are simply part of a much larger land-mass which was once attached to North America around the end of Precambrian times, some 570 million years ago.

The Lewisian Gneiss forms a **basement complex** of intensely deformed and metamorphosed rocks, cut by igneous intrusions of very different ages, which are themselves often deformed and metamorphosed in their turn. It is not a geological formation in the ordinary sense of the term, as the officers of the Geological Survey first recognised around the turn of this century. The results of radiometric dating, using the natural breakdown of radioactive elements in a rock to find its age, now show that the Lewisian Gneiss had a very long and complex history. Dating back to 2900 million years ago, or even earlier, the evolution of these basement gneisses continued until around 1400 million years ago. This history therefore represents nearly a third of all geological time since the Earth was itself formed, around 4600 million years ago.

The Lewisian Gneiss often presents the casual observer with a bewildering sense of geological chaos, even within a single exposure. However, it is fortunate for our understanding of this complex that it was intruded by a swarm of igneous dykes, mostly of basic or ultrabasic rocks, around 2400 million years ago. These intrusions can clearly be seen on the Ten-Mile Map of the Geological Survey, trending northwest-southeast across the Lewisian Gneiss between Loch Laxford and the district of Torridon, much farther to the south. They are known as the **Scourie Dykes**, after the village of the same name, just south of Loch Laxford, where a particularly good example can be seen. Their presence allows the two most important episodes in the evolution of the Lewisian Gneiss to be clearly distinguished from one another.

SCOURIAN GNEISSES. Where the Scourie Dykes retain their original features, so that they can be recognised as igneous intrusions cutting discordantly across the Lewisian Gneiss, they evidently have not been affected by any subsequent deformation or metamorphism. The gneisses intruded by these dykes must therefore be even older, forming what the Geological Survey originally described as a "fundamental complex". These very old gneisses are now called **Scourian**, dating back around 2700 million years, when they were intensely deformed and metamorphosed under extreme conditions, perhaps corresponding to depths as great as 60 kilometres within the Earth's crust. They occur as pyroxene-granulites, consisting of dark and greasy-looking feldspars together with blue opalescent quartz, which gets its milky appearance from the presence of minute needles of rutile within the crystals. Pyroxene rather than hornblende or biotite occurs within these gneisses, as the metamorphism occurred under anhydrous conditions, driving out any water that was once present in these deep-seated rocks.

LAXFORDIAN GNEISSES. However, where the Scourie Dykes have been so deformed and metamorphosed along with their country-rocks, that they can no longer be recognised as discrete intrusions, it is clear that the Lewisian Gneiss has been affected by relatively more recent events in its history. This frequently results in the Scourie Dykes becoming completely incorporated into the surrounding gneisses, so that they now just occur as rather more basic layers within the complex as a whole. The original gneisses also take on an entirely new character, undergoing further deformation and metamorphism under hydrous conditions. These changes break down the pyroxenes found in the Scourian Gneisses to form hornblende and biotite. This later reworking of the "fundamental complex" results in virtually new rocks, known as **Laxfordian** after the locality of Laxford Bridge. They mostly occur as hornblende-gneisses, intruded by much granitic material, often in the form of very coarse-grained pegmatite veins. The results of radiometric dating suggest that the Laxfordian events mostly occurred around

TORRIDONIAN SANDSTONE

1800 million years ago, even although some late intrusions give dates around 1400 million years ago.

TORRIDONIAN SANDSTONE.

Resting with a very profound unconformity on top of the Lewisian Gneiss lies the **Torridonian Sandstone.** This break in the geological record marks a time when the Lewisian Gneiss underwent a vast amount of uplift and erosion, eventually exposing rocks at the surface that were once buried at a depth of many kilometres. All this erosion did not reduce these rocks to a flat-lying surface, but left a landscape of considerable relief, carved into the Lewisian Gneiss. The Torridonian Sandstone was then deposited unconformably on top of these basement rocks, burying this ancient landscape under a flat-lying and very thick accumulation of sedimentary rocks.

Although the Torridonian Sandstone was once thought to form but a single sequence, two distinct groups are now recognised, namely an older Stoer Group and the younger Torridon Group, differing in age by nearly 200 million years. The **Stoer Group** was deposited around 995 million years ago, some 400 million years after the Lewisian Gneiss reached the end of its geological evolution, while the **Torridon Group** was laid down nearly 200 million years later, around 810 million years ago. Despite this difference in age, the two groups consist of sedimentary rocks, very much like one another.

The lowermost beds of the Stoer Group are breccias and conglomerates, banked as screes and alluvial fans against hills of Lewisian Gneiss. These rocks pass upwards into red sandstones and mudstones, probably laid down by braided rivers flowing from much higher ground to the northwest across wide flood-plains, There are also some limestones, most likely deposited in salt-lakes.

The Stoer Group was then tilted 30 degrees towards the northwest, prior to the deposition of the Torridon Group, some 810 million years ago. Consisting of a very thick sequence of red sandstones, rich in detrital feldspar, the Torridon Group can be traced from Cape Wrath in the far north as far as Rhum, lying off the Isle of Skye, some 120 miles to the south.

Although the Torridon Group rests unconformably on top of the Stoer Group in some places, it is usually found in contact with the Lewisian Gneiss. The unconformity at its base has only a little relief in the far north, where the underlying gneiss is often weathered to a depth of quite a few feet, forming an ancient soil-profile. Farther south, however, impressive hills of Lewisian Gneiss are found, rising to a height of 2000 feet above their surroundings on occasion, and blanketed by the sedimentary rocks of the Torridon Group. Where these rocks have been stripped off the Lewisian Gneiss by recent erosion, this ancient landscape is laid bare, exposed to our view at the present day. Even the valleys once cut into this pre-Torridonian landscape have been exhumed in some places, so that they are now followed by the present-day rivers.

The lowermost sediments of the Torridon Group are very diverse. Coarse breccias occur as scree deposits, banked against the underlying gneiss. They pass upwards into flaggy red sandstones with ripple-marks, together with grey shales showing dessication cracks and ripple-marks. All these rocks are overlain by a very thick and rather monotonous sequence of very coarse-grained and often pebbly sandstones, interbedded with more conglomeratic layers. These pebbly sandstones are best described as arkoses, rich in potash feldspar, which are usually dark red or chocolate brown in colour. They were derived from a mountainous area to the northwest as it underwent much physical weathering in response to rapid uplift and erosion, and then deposited by braided rivers flowing away from these mountains.

CAMBRO-ORDOVICIAN SEQUENCE.

After the deposition of the Torridon Group, earth-movements again affected the Northwest Highlands, prior to the accumulation of more sedimentary rocks during Cambrian and Ordovician times. These movements had the effect of tilting the Torridonian Sandstone away from the horizontal. A long period of erosion then ensued, after which there was a major transgression of the sea across this region at the start of Cambrian times, around 570 million years ago. The lowermost beds of the **Cambro-Ordovician** sequence were then laid down under marine conditions, forming the white and very conspicuous **Cambrian Quartzite**, which is often seen capping the mountains of Torridonian Sandstone. Typically, this quartzite displays cross-bedding, while there is often a slightly conglomeratic horizon at its very base.

The quartzite now dips at 10 or 20 degrees towards the east, while the Torridonian Sandstone below the unconformity is flat-lying. As it must have been deposited very close to the horizontal, this can only mean that the Torridonian Sandstone once dipped at a similar angle towards the west, prior to the deposition of this quartzite. Locally, it cuts across the Torridonian Sandstone, coming to rest directly on top of the Lewisian Gneiss, so forming what has been called the "**double unconformity**" of the Northwest Highlands.

The Cambrian Quartzite passes upwards into an equally quartzitic horizon, known as the **Pipe Rock.** This displays throughout its thickness a multitude of worm burrows, all cutting across the bedding at right angles. Some burrows have a simple pipe-like shape, much less than an inch across, while others display more the form of a funnel, so that they are more like a trumpet, opening upwards.

The Pipe Rock is overlain by the **Fucoid Beds.** This distinctive horizon, usually less than 60 feet thick, consists of brown-weathering dolomitic shales, together with some rather more sandy layers, which often show ripple-marks and cross-bedding.. It gets its name from the worm burrows commonly seen along the bedding, once identified as the markings made by sea-weed. The **Serpulite Grit** then forms a very persistent horizon of dolomitic quartzite, even thinner than the Fucoid Beds. As the name suggests, some beds are particularly coarse-grained for a sandstone. It carries abundant **Salterella**, which is a very small worm-like organism, originally identified as **Serpulites.**

Overlying the Serpulite Grit comes a great thicknress of the **Durness Limestone.** Despite the name, it is nearly all dolomite. Where fossils are found, they show that the lower part of the Durness Limestone belongs to the Lower Cambrian, while the upper parts are more likely to be Ordovician in age.

MOINE THRUST.

Separating all these rocks from the rest of the Scottish Highlands is the **Moine Thrust.** Dipping at a very low angle under the rocks lying to the east, this carries on its back metamorphic rocks known as the Moine Schists. These rocks have been thrust westwards for tens of miles over the underlying rocks towards the end of Silurian times, some 400 million years ago. This marked the end of the Caledonian earth-movements where they affected the rocks of the Scottish Highlands.

These movements also affected the rocks lying just below the Moine Thrust. As it continued, the thrusting gradually extended farther towards the northwest, overriding the underlying rocks in such a way that they were caught up more and more by the movements. The effect was much like snow piling up in front of a snow-plough. This produced a belt of complex thrusting and folding, up to several miles in width, which affects the rocks now exposed to the northwest, below the Moine Thrust itself. However, these movements died away towards the northwest, leaving the Northwest Highlands unaffected by the Caledonian earth-movements. This region now forms what is known as the **foreland** to the Caledonian Mountains, which lie to the southeast of the Moine Thrust.

MOINE SCHISTS.

Lying to the east of the Moine Thrust is a vast area of metamorphic rocks, underlying most of the Northern Highlands and extending across the Great Glen into the Grampian Highlands to the southeast. These rocks are known as the **Moine Schists.** They display a distinctly monotonous character throughout the whole of their outcrop. Typically, they were once sedimentary rocks, varying in composition from impure sandstones to shales and mudstones, now deformed and metamorphosed as the result of subsequent earth-movements.

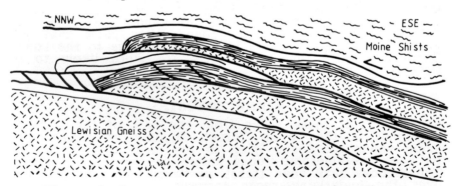

Figure 4. Cross-section through the Moine Thrust.

DALRADIAN SCHISTS

The more shaly rocks have been converted into mica-schists, sometimes rich in garnet and other metamorphic minerals, while the impure sandstones have often just been affected by recrystallisation to form rather massive rocks, rich in quartz and feldspar, together with some mica. Although these rocks are not very schistose, they are quite the commonest rock-type making up the Moine Schists as a whole.

The rather monotonous character of the Moine Schists conceals a long and complex history, to judge from the results of radiometric dating. This suggests that major earth-movements affected what has been called the **Older Moine** around 1000 million years ago, while pegmatites cutting these rocks were intruded around 750 million years ago. Such evidence implies that the Older Moine was deposited prior to 1000 million years ago, well before the Torridonian Sandstone. However, it also serves to distinguish these rocks from what has been termed the **Younger Moine**, which apparently passes up into the more recent rocks of the Dalradian Series without any break.

DALRADIAN SCHISTS.

Overlying the Moine Schists of the Grampian Highlands are the **Dalradian Schists**, exposed over a wide area to the southeast. They form a very varied sequence of sedimentary rocks, which was deformed and metamorphosed at the very end of Precambrian times, some 600 million years ago, according to the most recent research. There are quartzites present at various horizons throughout this sequence, although their place is taken by schistose grits in the Upper Dalradian. Limestones are also a common feature of the sequence, except that they are only found in the Lower and Middle Dalradian. They are metamorphosed to marbles in many places. Shaly rocks originally occurred at virtually all levels within the sequence, but they are now converted into slates, phyllites or schists, according to the intensity of the metamorphism. These rocks sometimes occur as black graphitic-schists, but more commonly as garnet mica-schists.

There are two other very distinctive horizons also present within the Dalradian sequence. Firstly, a **boulder-bed** is found just above the top of the Lower Dalradian, representing the deposits of an ice-sheet, grounded on the floor of a shallow sea. It carries boulders of granite in its upper levels. Secondly, there is a volcanic horizon marking the eruption of **pillow lavas,** just above the top of the Middle Dalradian. Such rocks are formed where molten lava is erupted on the sea-floor. As the lava comes into contact with the sea-water, its surface cools rapidly to form a glassy selvedge. This then bursts under pressure, allowing a bulbous protusion of lava to form, which then solidifies as a pillow-shaped mass of igneous rock. The underlying Dalradian rocks are also intruded by a great volume of igneous rocks, mostly in the form of basic sills, which are now deformed and metamorphosed along with their country-rocks during an early stage of the Caledonian earth-movements.

CALEDONIAN GRANITES.

The Moine and Dalradian rocks of the Scottish Highlands are intruded by a great many granites. They are not all the same age. The earliest granites are found all mixed up with their metamorphic country-rocks in a very intimate fashion, forming what are known as **migmatites.** The granite usually occurs as irregular veins of quartz and feldspar, separating thin stringers of highly metamorphosed country-rock from one another. Often these veins are folded along with their country-rocks, while other veins may cut across the whole complex in an irregular fashion. The country-rocks are alway highly metamorphosed, so that they are now gneisses rather than schists.

Apart from these migmatites, the other **granites** found in the Scottish Highlands were mostly intruded after the peak of regional metamorphism had passed. Typically, they form discrete intrusions, often of large size, cutting across the structures found in their country-rocks. They vary widely in age, some dating back around 650 million years, while others were only intruded by the start of Devonian times, around 395 million years ago. This phase of igneous activity therefore lasted for over 250 million years. The intrusion of the most recent granites at least was accompanied by volcanic eruptions at the surface.

OLD RED SANDSTONE.

Resting unconformably on the Highland Schists are the Devonian rocks of the **Old Red Sandstone.** These sediments were deposited under continental conditions on the eroded roots of the Caledonian mountains. The oldest rocks are found in the Southwest Highlands, where they were laid down as conglomerates and sandstones just before the eruption of the **Lorne Lavas** in Lower Old Red Sandstone times. These lavas are mostly andesites and basalts, up to 2000 feet in thickness. Volcanic rocks of a similar age are found at Glencoe and Ben Nevis, preserved as the result of cauldron-subsidence.

The Old Red Sandstone is also found in the Northern Highlands, along the western shores of the Moray Firth, and extending into the county of Caithness. However, these are younger rocks, mostly belonging to the Middle Devonian, with only a thin sequence of Lower Old Red Sandstone conglomerates and breccias present at their base. The **Middle Old Red Sandstone** accumulated to a very great thickness in the sedimentary basin known as **Lake Orcadie.** This formed a vast sheet of shallow and often rather brackish water, to which the sea never had access. Apart from breccias and conglomerates, which were deposited as screes and alluvial fans around the margins of Lake Orcadie, the sequence consists mostly of flagstones. These rocks were laid down as thinly-bedded repetitions of fine-grained sandstone, siltstone and mudstone, together with calcareous mudstone and flaggy limestone. The more calcareous horizons contain the sparse remains of a great many primitive fish. The whole sequence is overlain by more massive sandstones, laid down by rivers bringing an influx of coarser sediment into the area.

TRIASSIC AND JURASSIC SEDIMENTS.

Following the deposition of the Old Red Sandstone in Devonian times, which ended around 345 million years ago, there was a long gap in the geological record of the Scottish Highlands. Carboniferous rocks are virtually lacking, while it is difficult to distinguish any Permian rocks present within the area from overlying rocks of Triassic age. Together, these Permo-Triassic rocks represent the **New Red Sandstone,** found only locally along the shores of the Moray Firth, but occurring in greater force around the Tertiary Volcanic Complexes of Skye, Mull and Ardnamurchan. Conglomerates and sandstones are found, passing up into Jurassic rocks.

The start of Jurassic times around 195 million years ago was marked by the sea spreading around the fringes of the Scottish Highlands. A thick **Jurassic sequence** of marine and some deltaic sediments was then laid down,

TERTIARY IGNEOUS ACTIVITY

particularly on Skye, consisting mostly of sandstones, limestones and shales. The sandstones were deposited as deltas, built out across the sea-floor, where otherwise limestones and shales were accumulating. However, estuarine or lagoonal conditions became established for a period during the middle of Jurassic times. All these rocks are often packed with fossils, including corals, bivalves, ammonites, belemnites and brachiopods. A unique feature is seen around Portgower on the western shores of the Moray Firth, where **boulder-beds** are found as an integral part of the Jurassic sequence. They consist of a jumbled mass of angular boulders, all belonging to the Middle Old Red Sandstone, which slid down a submarine fault-scarp as the result of earth-quakes.

TERTIARY IGNEOUS ACTIVITY.

There are very few Cretaceous rocks preserved in the Scottish Highlands, although it is thought that the Chalk was once deposited over much if not all of this area. Instead, **Tertiary lavas** rest directly on the Jurassic sediments just described from the Inner Hebrides. These rocks are witness to a dramatic episode in the geological history of the Scottish Highlands, when volcanoes erupted on Skye, Rhum, Ardnamurchan, Mull and Arran, around 60 million years ago.

The earliest volcanic rocks are mostly basalt lavas and occasional tuffs, poured out over an ancient land-surface, so that they now lie unconformably on top of the older Jurassic rocks. They were probably erupted from volcanic vents, situated where the so-called central complexes are now found. These eruptions built up great thicknesses of lava-flows, forming much of Mull, Morvern and Northern Skye, together with the islands of Eigg, Muck and Canna, where they have been preserved from the effects of later erosion. Each lava-flow is rarely more than 50 feet thick, and one example has been traced for a distance of 13 miles. The tops of the lava-flows are often reddened by subaerial weathering under the tropical climate of Early Tertiary times.

This volcanic phase was followed by intrusion of the igneous rocks that now form the **central complexes** of Skye, Rhum, Ardnamurchan and Mull, as well as St Kilda and Arran. It is likely that this phase of igneous activity was accompanied by further outpourings of lava at the surface, but of this there is no direct evidence. Certainly, these intrusive complexes must represent the roots of ancient volcanoes as they continued to erupt. Broadly speaking, they show an early phase of explosive activity, followed by the intrusion of basic and ultrabasic rocks like gabbro and peridotite. The closing stages in their evolution were often marked by the intrusion of more acid rocks such as granite. Dykes were also intruded in a northwesterly direction during this phase of intrusive activity, forming a **Tertiary dyke-swarm** that can be traced from Northeast England to the Outer Hebrides. All this igneous activity was closely associated with the initial stages in the opening of the North Atlantic Ocean, as Northwest Europe parted company with Greenland.

PLEISTOCENE GLACIATION.

Since the ending of volcanic activity in Earlt Tertiary times, some 50 million years ago, the Scottish Highlands have been affected by widespread uplift and erosion. Since the sedimentary basin now formed by the North Sea subsided at the same time, it seems most likely that these movements were accompanied by a tilting of the whole land-mass towards the east. Certainly, it appears that a land-surface was established in Late Tertiary times, sloping gently towards the North Sea, across which rivers flowed in the same direction from a watershed in the west. Renewed pulses of uplift probably resulted in quite a mountainous topography, which was then accentuated by the effects of the **Pleistocene Glaciation.** This began around 2 million years ago, and continued intermittently until the very end of what is known popularly as the Great Ice Age, just 10,000 years ago.

The effects of this glaciation are seen nearly everywhere in the landscape of the Scottish Highlands. Glaciers in flowing downhill under the influence of gravity are able to attack the underlying rocks in two distinct ways. First, the ice has a "plucking" action, detaching blocks of rock along joints and other fractures, and then incorporating these blocks into the glacier as another addition to its load of rock fragments and other detritus. Second, the ice has a "scouring" effect as it drags its load of rock fragments over the solid rocks forming its floor, grinding down this surface by abrasion.

Landforms produced by glacial erosion are a characteristic feature of the higher ground in the Scottish Highlands. Many valleys have the U-shaped profiles typical of **glacial**

troughs, with steep hillsides sweeping down to form flat-bottomed valleys. These valleys are often eroded along their lengths into a series of **rock basins,** now occupied by lochs, often very deep, separated from one another by a series of rocky steps. Where these glacial troughs reach the coast, particularly in the west, they are likely to be occupied by arms of the sea, forming **fjords** or **sea-lochs.** Although the glaciers eroding these valleys mostly flowed away from the higher ground in response to gravity, this was not always the case. In particular, the ice was at its thickest just to the east of the present-day watershed, forcing it to flow uphill to the west in some places. The glacial troughs eroded by this ice are then said to breach the watershed.

The heads of glacial valleys are often bounded by steep slopes. **Corries** have much the same shape, formed as the ice accumulated on the upper slopes of the mountains. Typically, they look like giant amphitheatres, backed by steep cliffs. Often, their floors are occupied by a small lake, dammed by solid rock or by glacial deposits. Where two corries occur close together, they may only be separated from one another by a narrow ridge known as an **arete.** Sharp peaks are formed wherever these ridges converge on one another, surrounded by corries which have cut into the mountain from several sides at once.

The effects of glacial erosion may also be seen wherever solid rocks are exposed. Often, these rocks are scoured and eroded by the ice to form **glacial pavements.** There are **striations** or **glacial striae** sometimes visible on these surfaces, where slight grooves and scratches have been made by rock fragments as they were dragged along by the ice. Occasionally, these surfaces were moulded by the ice into more extreme forms, known as **roche moutonnees.** These have elongate and streamlined shapes, gracefully rounded with smooth contours facing upstream against the flow of the ice. Downstream, they often end steeply in an abrupt step, formed where the rock has been plucked away by the ice.

While glacial erosion was the dominant process to affect the higher ground during the Last Glaciation, its place was taken by deposition once the ice flowed out beyond the mountains. **Boulder clay** was deposited widely over the lower ground, not only obscuring the pre-existing topography but also giving its own characteristic landforms. These deposits typically consist of scattered boulders of all shapes and sizes, lying in a gritty clay. It mostly accumulated below the ice-sheet, plastering the underlying surface with detritus. Boulder clay often forms a dull and featureless landscape, only enlivened where it becomes more rolling in character, with slight hills and shallow valleys. Lochs are formed where the water cannot drain away from any slight depressions in such an undulating surface. Elsewhere, **drumlins** are found where boulder clay is thrown into smooth but elongate mounds, up to 100 feet high in some cases, giving rise to a landscape thought to resemble a "basket of eggs."

Much detritus was also dumped by the glaciers where the ice finally melted along its front. Where this ice-front remained stationary, so that the glaciers were neither advancing nor retreating, **terminal moraines** are found as distinct ridges of sand and gravel, often with larger boulders. More common are the much wider spreads of **hummocky moraine,** dumped where it lies as the glaciers gradually retreated, or just left by the melting away of "dead ice", once the glaciers had ceased to advance. As the glaciers retreated towards the end of the Great Ice Age, vast volumes of melt-water were released, carrying along sand and gravel as well as much finer material in suspension. The coarser detritus was deposited as **fluvio-glacial sands and gravels,** which often choke the lower reaches of the valleys draining the Scottish Highlands.

The Last Glaciation was also accompanied by the removal of sea-water from the oceans to form vast ice-sheets, which caused the Earth's surface to subside under their weight. Quite large changes in sea-level occurred as a result. However, the melting of the ice-sheets restored the sea to its original volume, while the land is still now only just recovering from the weight of the ice. This means that the land is still rising, so that the sea once stood much higher in comparison with the land, just after the end of the Last Glaciation. **Raised beaches** are therefore a common feature of the coasts around the Scottish Highlands, particularly in the southwest. These features are best seen where they are cut into solid rock, forming wavecut platforms lying well above the present level of the sea, backed by ancient cliffs. Caves, natural arches and sea-stacks may all be preserved, together with beach deposits.

HIGHLAND GEOLOGY TRAIL

INVERNESS TO JOHN O'GROATS.

The trail starts at Inverness, following the A9 road for most of the way to John O'Groats, apart from the occasional detour. The route keeps to the low ground along the western shores of the Moray Firth, except where it climbs over the Ord of Caithness at the Sutherland border. Nearly all this ground is underlain by Devonian rocks of the Middle Old Red Sandstone, but there is a thin strip of Triassic and Jurassic rocks between Golspie and Helmsdale. The Moine Schists make up the higher ground of the Northern Highlands to the northwest, apart from the Lower Old Red Sandstone, which locally forms the foothills to this mountainous region. The Moine Schists are intruded by various granites, among which the Helmsdale Granite is the most conspicuous.

Boulder clay blankets much of the lower ground along the route, giving rise to a typical landscape of smooth contours and very subdued features, which can be seen in crossing the Black Isle and the interior of Caithness, away from the coast. However, there are also widespread deposits of sand and gravel, laid down as the glaciers retreated, perhaps best-seen in Easter Ross and farther north beyond the Dornoch Firth. Raised beaches are a common feature along the coast-line, occurring at various heights above sea-level. The lowest and most recent often gives rise to very wide areas of flat-lying land.

Although the scenery lacks the splendour seen in the Northwest Highlands, this part of the trail provides an excellent introduction to geology in the field.

INVERNESS TO TARBAT NESS.

Leave Inverness northbound on the A9, crossing the Beauly Firth by the Kessock bridge. The coast of the Black Isle to the northeast is remarkably straight, determined as it is by the line of the Great Glen Fault, lying just offshore to the southeast. The effect of the Great Glen Fault can be seen in the shattered nature of the Middle Old Red Sandstone conglomerates, where they exposed in roadcuts along the A9 just across the bridge. Similar rocks are exposed on the shore at **Craigton** [NH 663485], which can be reached by turning south off the A9 and driving along the B9161 through the village of North Kessock itself.

Continue across the Black Isle, following the A9 to reach the road junction for Evanton on the north side of the Cromarty Firth, where a visit can be made to the **Black Rock Gorge.** This spectacular feature is reached by diving through the village of Evanton on the old A9 and turning left just beyond the bridge over the River Glass along the road which runs up Glen Glass. After about a mile, a rough track on the left leads down towards the river, which runs in a deep and very narrow cleft for a distance of nearly a mile. A foot-bridge crosses the gorge at [NH 593668], and provides an excellent viewpoint. This gorge was cut by waters from melting glaciers towards the end of the Last Glaciation. Its fern-covered walls are formed by Old Red Sandstone breccias, crudely bedded and nearly horizontal. Return to Evanton, and turn left along the old A9 to regain the main road near Alness.

Alternatively, a visit may be made to **Hugh Miller's Birthplace** at Cromarty on the Black Isle, by taking the B9163 to the right just before the bridge over the Cromarty Firth is reached. Hugh Miller (1802-1856) was a stonemason to trade with an world-wide reputation as a geologist. He eventually became the editor of an evangelical newspaper published in Edinburgh, which carried his essays on geology as well as book reviews and political articles. The cottage where he was born is now in the hands of the National Trust for Scotland. It houses a small selection of the fossils collected by him, as well as other relics of his remarkable life. A ferry runs in the summer across the Cromarty Firth to Nigg from where a cross-country route can be followed to reach the B9165 beyond Hill of Fearn.

On joining the A9 near Alness after visiting the Black Rock Gorge, follow this road as far north as its junction with the B9165, a few miles beyond Kildary. Turn right and then follow the B9165 through Hill of Fearn towards Portmahomack. **Tarbat Ness** is reached by taking the right fork just before entering this village. Stop in the car-park on the right of the private road leading to the lighthouse.

GEOLOGICAL LOCALITY: TARBAT NESS.

Descend to a narrow inlet [NH 945873] with a storm beach at its back immediately northeast of the car-park. There is a rough path leading down to the shore. The rocks belong to the Middle Old Red Sandstone. They are mostly red sandstones with scattered pebbles of white quartzite, although occasional horizons are creamy yellow. The quartz grains forming these sandstones can easily be seen on a weathered surface by using a hand-lens. The bedding is inclined away from the horizontal so that it now dips at 20 degrees towards the northwest. Cross-bedding is a common feature of these sandstones, showing that they were deposited by currents flowing from the southwest. Convolute bedding is also present, affecting the cross-bedded units.

Return to the car-park, and walk along the track past the lighthouse to the headland of Tarbat Ness itself. This provides a splendid panorama on a fine day, stretching from Buchan right round the shores of the Moray Firth to Caithness. The rocks exposed at the headland are pebbly yellow sandstones, quarried in the past for millstones, to judge by a reject lying close to the end of the track.

TARBAT NESS TO PORTGOWER.

Returning through Portmahomack, take the right fork about 2 miles beyond the village, leading towards Tain. After passing through Tain, turn right along the A9, just beyond the town. At the time of writing, the Dornoch bridge is still under construction, so a detour needs to be made around the Dornoch Firth through Bonar Bridge. However, once it is open, cross this bridge, and continue north along the A9 towards Loch Fleet.

Crossing the head of **Loch Fleet** provides an excellent view of a glaciated landscape, where erosion has prevailed over deposition. Strath Fleet has the typical U-shaped form of a glacial trough, even although its flat floor is covered by river deposits. The hills guarding its mouth are formed by rather massive breccias of the Middle Old Red Sandstone, scraped bare by the ice, leaving steep outcrops of glacially-scoured rock. Several of these hills have the form of "roche moutonnees" on a grand scale, since ice flowing from the northwest has plucked away at the rocks to leave the steepest slopes facing southeast.

Stop just north of **The Mound** at a layby on the A9, about 200 yards beyond its junction with the A839, to examine the breccias forming these glaciated slopes at the roadside. They consist of angular fragments of impure grey quartzite and pink granite, set in a much finer-grained matrix of reddish purple sandstone. These pebbles have surfaces stained purple, and they are packed tightly together in the rock. These breccias were probably laid down as scree deposits along the flanks of a mountainous area, formed by the Highland Schists.

Drive north along the A9 through Golspie, where a stop can be made at the **Orcadian Stone Company,** situated on the main street just beyond the Bank of Scotland. There is a splendid exhibition of mineral specimens from all over the world, and a display of geological specimens illustrating the local geology. Books and maps can be purchased, as well as mineral and rock specimens.

The route now passes from the Old Red Sandstone on to a narrow strip of Triassic and Jurassic rocks, which lies along the coast for nearly 20 miles as far north as the Ord of Caithness. These rocks are mostly sandstones, limestones and shales, downthrown along the Helmsdale Fault against the more resistant rocks to the northwest. These mostly consist of the Middle Old Red Sandstone, except that the Helmsdale Granite appears farther northeast around Helmsdale. Much of the lower ground is mantled by thick deposits of sand and gravel, while there are long stretches of raised beach along the coast, particularly conspicuous at Brora. Coal has been mined from the Jurassic rocks at Brora since 1529, although this has now been abandoned.

Continuing north along the A9, the village of **Portgower** is reached some 9 miles beyond Brora. Take the second turning to the right after entering the village. Turn to the right after 50 yards, and drive to the end of the road, where cars may be parked.

GEOLOGICAL LOCALITY: PORTGOWER.

It is essential to visit this locality at low tide. Walk 100 yards southeast down a track towards the sea from the end of the road, and follow this track as it turns right in its descent to the coast. After crossing the railway line, walk southwest along the shore for 200 yards to reach the ruins of a wall. Just beyond this point, the coast forms a low promontory [ND 004127] running out to sea at low tide. Its farthest point is the Fallen Stack of Portgower. The rocks are Jurassic in age. They consist of a series of boulder beds in which large blocks of Middle Old Red Sandstone rocks are embedded, surrounded by a matrix of shelly calcareous grit. These boulders are rather angular in shape, and vary greatly in size. They consist of rocks typical of the Caithness Flagstones, and carry fish remains as fossils which identify them as Middle Old Red

31

Sandstone. An excellent example of just such a boulder bed is found immediately below high water mark, while another lies slightly farther offshore. This horizon carries large boulders up to 10 yards in length. Since the boulders consist of well-bedded rocks, it can be seen how they are completely disorientated, forming a higgledy-piggledy jumble of angular blocks. By way of contrast, the sequence as a whole dips southeast at a low angle.

By scrambling across these rocks, the Fallen Stack of Portgower can itself be reached. This forms a huge block of Middle Old Red Sandstone, measuring nearly 50 yards in length and 30 yards in width. Its bedding is close to the vertical, striking at a high angle to the overall dip of the beds. The interpretation placed on all these boulder beds is that they were deposited at the foot of a submarine escarpment in Jurassic times, which was first formed and then maintained by repeated movements along the Helmsdale Fault. Large blocks of Caithness Flagstone became detached at the top of this submarine escarpment, sliding and perhaps tumbling down this unstable slope into the deeper waters at its foot. This probably occurred in response to earthquake shocks along the Helmsdale Fault itself.

PORTGOWER TO SOUTH HEAD OF WICK.

The route from Portgower first passes through Helmsdale, where a detour can be made up the Strath of Kildonan to visit **Baile an Or** (the town of gold), where the gold-rush of 1869 took place. Continue north along the A9 road from Helmsdale over the Ord of Caithness. Just beyond **Navidale**, typical exposures of Helmsdale Granite are seen on the hillside above the road. Once the higher ground is reached beyond the old county boundary, the road crosses and recrosses the unconformity separating the Helmsdale Granite from the overlying Old Red Sandstone. Although this unconformity is exposed in a series of roadcuts, it is difficult to locate, as the overlying sediments are arkoses, looking much like the underlying granite from which they were derived. These sediments pass upwards into well-bedded sandstones and shales, which dip north at a gentle angle away from the underlying granite.

Once past Ousdale, the quartzite ridge of Scaraben comes into view with its grey screes, quite unlike the more rounded hills formed by the Helmsdale Granite to the south. The road then descends abruptly at Berriedale, only to climb back north to its previous level. Beyond are rolling moorlands of boulder clay, reaching the sea in steep if not vertical cliffs along the coast. Indeed, the coast is mostly inaccessible to the north of the Ord, except where rivers have cut deep valleys right down to sea-level. This landscape is typical of Caithness as a whole. Nearly all the county is underlain by the Caithness Flagstones, belonging to the Middle Old Red Sandstone. However, these rocks are mostly mantled by thick deposits of boulder clay, except on the higher ground, so that inland there are few features of geological interest.

Driving north, the Caithness Flagstones are well-exposed in roadcuts at the southern end of the **Dunbeath bypass,** just beyond the road junction [ND 154292]. The flat-lying bedding has a very flaggy appearance, while it is cut by sets of vertical joints, making the rocks appear like blocks of masonry. Beyond Dunbeath, stop at the **Laidhay Croft Museum,** where a splendid panorama looks out towards the west. The rounded ridge of Scaraben is seen end-on, flanked to the north by the conical peaks of Maiden Pap and Morven. Scaraben is quartzite, belonging to the Moine rocks of the Scottish Highlands, while Maiden Pap and Morven are built of Old Red Sandstone conglomerates and sandstones, so that differences in geology are expressed very directly in the topography.

Continue north along the A9 road past Thrumster, where a detour can be made to the coast at **Sarclet Haven** [ND 351433]. The rocks on the south side of the harbour are affected by a good example of a thrust fault. On entering the outskirts of Wick, turn right and follow the route signposted to the Old Castle of Wick. Park at the end of the road where it runs above the coast, just beyond the swimming pool, near the **South Head of Wick.**

GEOLOGICAL LOCALITY: SOUTH HEAD OF WICK.

Walk down a sloping bedding-plane to [ND 375493], where a vertical face is exposed just above high-water mark. Apart from the spectacular nature of this bedding-plane **(MFG 4),** dipping at a fairly shallow angle towards the north, the rocks also show a variety of other features. The vertical face already mentioned exposes thinly-bedded shales with some calcareous layers, passing upwards into grey siltstones and shales. Climbing up a near-vertical step reveals impressive arrays of sedimentary dykelets **(MFG 63),** which cut the shaly layers at a high angle to the bedding. They are composed of siltstone, penetrating downwards from thin beds of the same material.

These dykelets occupy what are known as synaeresis cracks, which are thought to form underwater by the contraction of muddy sediment in response to changes in salinity. Once formed, these gashes became filled with silty sediment, washed in when the overlying bed was deposited. Subsequently, these dykelets were folded as a response to the compaction which affected the whole sequence after its deposition. The dykelets (**MFG 62**) can be seen in plan where they are exposed on nearby bedding-planes. Although somewhat irregular, they tend to be roughly parallel to one another. They differ in this respect from sun-cracks, which typically have polygonal outlines, and which also occur on a much larger scale. Ripple-marks and occasional sun-cracks can also be seen on these bedding-planes.

The rocks are also well-jointed with two sets of vertical fractures cutting across the bedding, trending east-west and northwest-southeast, respectively. Thin veins of light-coloured calcite and brown-weathering dolomite occupy the latter set of veins. Opposite a small inlet, just a short distance to the north of the exposures just described, there is a vertical fault in the cliff, marked by the presence of veins of calcite and dolomite. The down-throw on this fault is 3 feet to the south, to judge by its effect on a massive bed at the top of the cliff.

Return to the main road, and take the A9 through the centre of Wick towards John O'Groats. The country north of Wick is low-lying, and sand-dunes are well-developed along the shores of Sinclair Bay. Farther north, however, the road climbs around Warth Hill, where the Orkney Islands are seen across the waters of the Pentland Firth. On reaching John O'Groats, park near the Last House.

GEOLOGICAL LOCALITY: NESS OF DUNCANSBY.

To reach the Ness of Duncansby [ND 391738], walk east along the coast from the Last House. The John O'Groats Fish Bed is exposed on the shore below high-water mark around 120 yards from the pier. It forms a calcareous horizon, creamy brown in colour. The rocks are otherwise mostly dull red sandstones, dipping northeast at a low angle, interbedded with reddish shales and siltstones.

GEOLOGICAL LOCALITY: DUNCANSBY HEAD

These rocks lack the flaggy character which is typical of the Caithness Flagstones. Passing around a slight bay, backed by a beach of shell sand, igneous rocks are first encountered just below high-water mark, some 50 yards beyond an old windlass. They are poorly exposed, forming a dyke of very dark rock, almost black in colour, which appears to cut across the bedding of the sandstones. Continue around the headland itself, beyond which a volcanic vent is clearly seen on the foreshore, surrounded by red sandstones.

The exposures found just below high-water mark at the edge of the beach clearly reveal the nature of the agglomerate lying within this vent. It forms a breccia with angular fragments up to 6 inches in length, set in a much finer-grained matrix of comminuted material, grey or purple in colour. Fragments of dark igneous rock are conspicuous, together with large pieces of an almost black mineral, probably augite, consisting of single crystals with cleavage planes that glint in the sun. There are also fragments of sandstone, limestone and gneiss. Although the contacts of this vent are not well-exposed, it forms an area about 200 yards across, quite distinct from the sandstones which make up its country-rocks.

GEOLOGICAL LOCALITY: DUNCANSBY HEAD.

The cliffs around Duncansby Head are vertical or even overhanging, and due care should be taken. Walk east around the coast to the Bay of Sannick, where the red sandstones are cut off by a fault. This strikes south of southeast across the peninsula separating Duncansby Head from the ground to the southwest. It brings up the Caithness Flagstones to the surface, where they form impressive cliffs around the headland itself.

Deep **geos** with vertical or even overhanging walls penetrate the headland where the sea has attacked the land along joints or faults in the flagstones. There are sea-caves at the back of these inlets wherever the sea is still active in its attack upon the land. Gaping chasms are found wherever the roofs of these caves have collapsed, leaving a bridge of rock across their seaward ends. As the cliffs continue to recede, sea-caves often join up to form natural arches, propping up the cliffs like flying buttresses. Where the arch itself collapses, a sea-stack is left standing offshore as a testimony to the power of the sea in wearing away the land. All these features can be seen in walking around Duncansby Head from the Bay of Sannick to the small bay [ND 403728] lying to its south, beyond The Knee.

Descend to the shore at the back of this small bay by a steep and rather rough path. This leads down a gully from the iron gate in the fence that skirts the cliff-top at this point. This gully is eroded out along the fault which cuts across the peninsula of Duncansby Head. On reaching the shore, it can be seen that the rocks exposed by the cliffs the left of this gully are rather massive red sandstones, similar to those found around John O'Groats. They are quite different from the typical flagstones that make up the cliffs on its other side. Since the bedding is flat-lying on both sides of the gully, a fault most likely runs down the gully, even though it is not exposed at this level.

In fact, just such a fault is exposed on the foreshore at low tide, where it is marked by a zone of shattering, about 10 feet in width. Looking north of northwest, it is clear that the flagstones turn down against this fault from the right, while the sandstones turn up as they approach the fault from the left. This suggests that the sandstones have been thrown down against the flagstones from a higher level, so that they are the younger rocks. The sandstones are also seen to be faulted where they are exposed in the cliff-face, 15 yards to the southwest of the gully. This fault dips steeply northeast, and downthrows about 8 feet in the same direction. This means that it is a normal fault, although it has the opposite sense of downthrow in comparison with the much larger fault that runs down the gully itself. Return to the car park at John O'Groats.

HIGHLAND GEOLOGY TRAIL

JOHN O'GROATS TO CAPE WRATH.

The north coast of Caithness and Sutherland provides an excellent cross-section through the Northern Highlands. Starting from John O'Groats, the trail first crosses the Middle Old Red Sandstone rocks which we have already encountered farther south. These sediments rest unconformably on the metamorphic and igneous rocks of the Scottish Highlands, quite spectacularly in places like Red Point and Portskerra. The trail then crosses the outcrop of the Highland Schists, where they reach the wild and very rocky coast of the north of Sutherland. These rocks are very complex. Although Moine Schists are present, they are associated with basement rocks of Lewisian aspect, which have undergone so much deformation and metamorphism that their original nature is open to doubt.

Farther west, however, the geology becomes less complex. There, the Moine Schists are found over a wide area, separated by fold-cores and thrust-slices of the Lewisian basement, now greatly reworked by the Caledonian deformation and metamorphism. All these rocks are thrust west of northwest over the underlying rocks of the Northwest Highlands by the Moine Thrust. This thrust outcrops around Loch Eriboll. Beyond lies a belt of disturbed rocks, carried forward of the thrust itself. The trail then reaches the northwestern foreland to the Caledonian belt, where Lewisian Gneiss, Torridonian Sandstone and the Cambro-Ordovician rocks are all preserved from the effects of the Caledonian earth-movements.

JOHN O'GROATS TO RED POINT.

Follow the A836 road west from John O'Groats towards Thurso. All this ground is covered by a thick blanket of boulder clay, which mostly obscures the underlying rocks of the Middle Old Red Sandstone except where they are exposed along the coast. At the village of Dunnet, a detour can be made to **Dunnet Head**, which is the most northerly point on the Scottish mainland. The rocks outcropping around this headland are red and yellow sandstones of the Upper Old Red Sandstone. They are much more resistant to weathering and erosion than the Middle Old Red Sandstone, against which they have been faulted. These sandstones can best be examined on the shore at the **Point of Ness** [ND 209711], where they display much cross-bedding, often affected by slumping. The cliffs north of this point clearly show the well-bedded character of these rocks.

Continue west around the shores of Dunnet Bay with its splendid fringe of sand-dunes, facing out over the waters of the Pentland Firth towards the northwest, towards Thurso. Between Castletown and Thurso, the road runs inland, but a detour can be made to visit **Clairdon Head** around [ND 138700], where sun-cracks (**MFG 61**) are particularly well-developed. This locality is best approached by taking the side road passing through West Murkle to the Haven.

Stop just after passing through Thurso on the A836, near the caravan site [ND 110689], where a good view can be seen across the bay to **Scrabster Harbour.** The harbour itself is backed by cliffs of boulder clay, forming steep slopes cut by gullies. The great thickness of boulder clay can easily be appreciated, as virtually no solid rock can be seen, except at the very foot of these slopes. Follow the A836 road past Dounreay to the village of Reay. The scenery changes once the sedimentary rocks of Caithness give way to the igneous and metamorphic rocks of the Scottish Highlands. This is marked around Reay by knolls of igneous rock, which appear as if stripped of their sedimentary veneer of Middle Old Red Sandstone rocks. Park at the viewpoint [ND 933646] on the north side of the road, just over 2 miles west of Reay.

GEOLOGICAL LOCALITY: RED POINT.

Although it can only be reached by walking over rough moorland, this splendid locality [ND 930659] easily repays the effort involved. **Great care should be taken where walking along the cliffs to the east of Red Point.** Start along a poor path 50 yards west of the layby, which heads north towards a heather-covered hillock in the distance. After nearly half a mile, follow a stream which runs northwest down a slight valley towards the sea, aiming for a grassy knoll. On reaching the cliff-top, about quarter of a mile to the east of Red Point, turn right and walk northeast towards the headland. The cliffs are vertical, capped with steep and slippery slopes of boulder clay. Well-bedded rocks of the Middle Old Red Sandstone are exposed along this coast, dipping gently towards the north. Offshore, there are several sea-stacks. Just before Red Point, the rocks can be examined in safety, once the cliffs fall away towards the sea.

GEOLOGICAL LOCALITY: RED POINT

The exposures just east of Red Point show grey fine-grained limestones overlain by coarse breccias. All these rocks are underlain by the flaggy sediments found farther along the coast towards the west. Traced east towards Red Point, these flagstones are replaced by coarse breccias, as can be seen on reaching the headland itself. These breccias weather out into a very knobbly surface. They consist of very angular fragments of granitic rock, up to a foot across at the very most, together with less common fragments of quartzose schist and vein quartz. These fragments are usually packed together in a felspar-rich matrix of gritty arkose. Locally, however, very fine-grained limestone acts as a cement.

All these rocks are banked unconformably against the coarse-grained granite which is exposed at Red Point itself. The actual contact is close to the vertical, and it can be traced right to the top of the cliffs. It is best exposed on a ledge running out to sea below a grassy slope, some 50 yards to the west of the headland. A thin selvedge of breccia can be traced along the contact, where it is plastered against the granite. Tongues of breccia can be traced along the bedding for short distances away from this contact, before wedging out as the breccias are replaced by flaggy sediments.

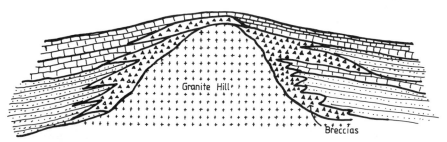

Figure 5. Vertical Cross-Section at Red Point.

Beyond this contact, granite is exposed as far as the headland itself, together with some enclaves of gneissose schist, cut by granitic veins. Just east of the headland, breccias are banked against the granite, wedging out as they are traced away from the unconformity. These fragmental rocks are interbedded with impure limestones, forming the bulk of the sequence at this point. However, these limestones are themselves underlain by quartzose sandstones carrying much detrital feldspar, evidently derived from the underlying granite. Clearly, the sedimentary rocks at Red Point buried a steep-sided hill of much older granite in Middle Old Red Sandstone times, which has now been partly exhumed from beneath its cover of screes, sandstones and flaggy limestones. Return to the road by walking south of southeast until the path is reached at the head of the shallow valley.

To reach the next locality, drive west along the A836, crossing the Halladale River with its terraces of fluvioglacial sands and gravels. After passing through Melvich, turn right at the hotel to reach Portskerra. Fork right, and park at a small group of houses near the coast. Walk down the track leading to the harbour.

GEOLOGICAL LOCALITY: PORTSKERRA.

This locality marks the western margin of the Orcadian Basin, where the Middle Old Red Sandstone can be seen resting unconformably on top of the metamorphic rocks of the Scottish Highlands. The irregular nature of this unconformity (**MFG 108**) can best be appreciated where it is exposed in the cliffs [NC 877665] to the north of the harbour, capped with boulder clay. The underlying rocks are schists and gneisses, intruded by granitic veins. They are exposed as two knolls, lying on either side of the bay. These rocks, pink in colour and lacking any bedding, are overlain unconformably by breccias and sandstones, belonging to the Middle Old Red Sandstone.

The well-marked bedding shown by these rocks is quite clearly draped over an irregular surface cut by erosion across the underlying rocks, forming a shallow syncline. Evidently, the sedimentary rocks buried an ancient landscape of low hills and valleys. By scrambling across the foreshore, this unconformity can be seen at close quarters (**MFG 105**). The metamorphic rocks are overlain by rubbly material, which passes up into a basal breccia. Granitic fragments are present in this breccia, clearly derived from the physical disintegration of the underlying rocks.

PORTSKERRA TO COLDBACKIE.

Returning to the main road, drive west along the A836 towards Bettyhill. Although the road first crosses ground heavily mantled with boulder clay, once beyond Strathy this gives way to a much more rocky landscape, where the glaciers have left little in the way of superficial deposits. Strathy itself lies on an outlier of Middle Old Red Sandstone, mostly sandstones and conglomerates, but metamorphic and igneous rocks appear in force farther to the west. These basement rocks can be seen by taking a rough track to the top of **Cnoc Mhor** [NC 757638], which leaves the main road just before the turning for Kirtomy, some 2½ miles beyond Armadale.

The exposures along the track just below the summit show excellent migmatites, in which irregular but very abundant veins of granitic material are intimately associated with coarse-grained but still schistose country-rocks (**MFG 243, 244 & 245**). The view from Cnoc Mhor is spectacular on a fine day, stretching from Dunnet Head and the Orkney Islands in the east to Whiten Head and the mountains of Ben Loyal, Ben Hope and Foinaven in the west. The twin peaks of Ben Griam Mhor and Ben Griam Beg stand out in the south as outliers of Middle Old Red Sandstone conglomerate, while Morvern is seen on the distant horizon. The extraordinary nature of the low plateau which makes up most of North Sutherland can clearly be appreciated from this view-point: it probably marks a surface of erosion exhumed from beneath a sedimentary cover of Old Red Sandstone rocks.

Return to the A836, and continue west through Bettyhill, where a well-developed terrace can be seen, lying around 50 feet above sea-level at the mouth of the River Naver. This forms the seaward end of a series of river terraces, constructed from fluvio-glacial sands and gravels, which can be traced in an irregular fashion down the valley of Strathnaver. Crossing the higher ground to the west, a detour can be made through **Skerray** by turning right along a side road to the north just after the A836 crosses the River Borgie.

This road follows a river terrace which can be traced down the River Borgie to the sea. Another terrace can be seen at exactly the same height on the other side of the valley. This terrace opens out to form a wide area of flat-lying ground, overlooking the mouth of the river around 50 feet above sea-level. Its seaward side is flanked by sand-dunes. This is a characteristic feature of this very exposed coast, where strong winds blowing off the sea can carry sand inland to heights of 400 feet, encouraging interesting communities of unusual plants as a result. Stop at a parking place [NC 680611], just after the road forks, and cross a footbridge over the River Borgie to reach **Torrisdale Beach.** The outcrops exposed to sand-blast at the back of this beach around [NC 689618] display impressive examples of folding (and boudinage), which affect a series of granitic veins cutting across the metamorphic rocks at this locality.

COLDBACKIE TO LOCH ERIBOLL.

Return to the road, and continue through Skerray to reach the main road, two miles east of Coldbackie. A stop can next be made just after this small hamlet, parking at the layby above **Coldbackie Bay** [NC 610601]. The roadcut just opposite this layby exposes excellent examples of fold mullions (**MFG 226**) in quartzo-felspathic schists, typical of the Moine rocks in this area. There is also a dramatic view of the steep cliffs formed by the massive conglomerates of Watch Hill, or Cnoc an Fhreiceadain. Although once thought to be Devonian, a Permo-Triassic age now appears more likely for these conglomerates. They can be examined in a shallow gully, just to the left of the path as it descends towards the beach. The unconformity made by these conglomerates with the underlying Moine Schists can be located within a few feet in a series of exposures at the back of this beach, close to its eastern end.

Continuing west, the main road becomes the A838 just before the village of Tongue. This road then crosses the Kyle of Tongue by a causeway. Ben Loyal makes a very conspicuous feature to the south with its deep corries and sharp rocky peaks. Its summit ridge is crowned by tors, making it unusual among Scottish mountains. It is formed by an intrusive mass of syenite, an igneous rock much like a true granite but lacking any quartz. Its distinctive features reflect its geological structure, quite unlike that of its surrounding country-rocks. These are the Moine Schists, which have taken on an easterly dip as the Moine Thrust is approached from this direction. This is also reflected in the surrounding landscape, which consists of a series of steep scarps facing towards the west, backed by

42

gentler dip-slopes descending towards the east. Ben Hope is merely the highest of these scarps, somewhat disguised by the deep corries on its eastern flanks.

West of the causeway, a detour can be made around the Kyle of Tongue to examine garnetiferous mica-schists in the exposures around the broch at **Kinloch**. Take the side road south along the western side of the Kyle of Tongue, and park at a sharp bend in the road [NC 554531], just below the broch where it overlooks the Kinloch River. Typical garnet-mica-schists are well-exposed along the path leading to the broch. The deep-red garnets resist weathering to stand out proud of the surface. Continue along this road through Kinloch towards Tongue, and rejoin the main road.

Instead of turning south along the western shore of the Kyle of Tongue, it is also possible to turn north along the road through Melness and Talmine. The bedding of the Moine Schists is folded where these rocks are exposed in the crags overlooking the road just east of **Loch Vasgo** [NC 581645], while the quartz-rodding (**MFG 227**) which affects the Moine rocks exposed around the summit of **Ben Hutig** [NC 538653] can be seen by climbing this hill from Achininver.

Back at the main road, drive west along the A838 across the wide and rather featureless moorland of A'Mhoine. Although the Moine Schists are poorly exposed, they are named after this locality, where they were first mapped by the Geological Survey. Their outcrop is bounded to the northwest by the Moine Thrust, which is crossed as the road descends towards Loch Hope. Although not exposed, it is known to dip towards the east of south-east at a shallow angle. The landscape changes dramatically to expose much more rock as this important dislocation is crossed. The first exposures encountered are Lewisian Gneiss, which forms the crags above Loch Hope. These rocks have been carried west on the Arnaboll Thrust, which lies underneath the Moine Thrust itself.

This thrust is exposed on Ben Arnaboll, where it makes a prominent feature in the crags overlooking the main road (see Figure 5). The rocks below this thrust are Cambrian quartzites belonging to the Pipe Rock. They are exposed over a wide area to the northwest of this thrust, lying mostly to the north of the A838, where they are clearly seen on the slopes of Ben Heilam. The road crosses over these quartzites to the west of Loch Hope, before it reaches an outcrop of Durness Limestone which runs along the eastern shore of Loch Eriboll. This limestone is first seen at a bend in the main road just after it passes Loch Ach'an Lochaidh. As Loch Eriboll comes into view, stop at the layby [NC 453601] overlooking Ard Neackie.

GEOLOGICAL PANORAMA: LOCH ERIBOLL.

Looking south towards the head of Loch Eriboll from this viewpoint provides an excellent cross-section across the Moine Thrust Belt. It shows how the Caledonian earth-movements have reversed the original succession of the rocks, bringing Cambrian Quartzite and Pipe Rock on top of Durness Limestone, and then Lewisian Gneiss on top of Cambrian Quartzite and Pipe Rock.

The hills lying to the northwest of Loch Eriboll are Cambrian Quartzite, resting unconformably on top of Lewisian Gneiss. These rocks mark the foreland to the Moine Thrust, unaffected by the Caledonian earth-movements. The eastern slopes of Carnstackie, Beinn Spionnaidh, Meall nan Cra and Meall Meadhonach are all dip-slopes of Cambrian Quartzite, capped in some cases by Pipe Rock, descending towards the shores of Loch Eriboll. Only the much rougher outlines of Beinn Ceannabeinne, lying just out of sight to the northeast, reveal the underlying Lewisian Gneiss.

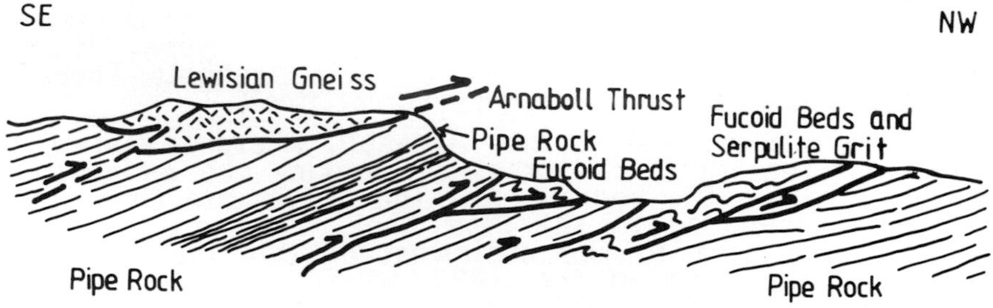

SE   NW

Lewisian Gneiss — Arnaboll Thrust
Pipe Rock
Fucoid Beds
Fucoid Beds and Serpulite Grit
Pipe Rock
Pipe Rock

Figure 6. View of the Arnaboll Thrust.

GEOLOGICAL PANORAMA: LOCH ERIBOLL

The lowermost thrust to affect the rocks of the Moine Thrust Belt lies hidden under the waters of Loch Eriboll. It brings Durness Limestone on top of Cambrian Quartzite and Pipe Rock. Where it is overlain by boulder clay around Eriboll House, this limestone gives fertile ground capable of cultivation. Its outcrop covers much of the lower ground along the eastern shores of Loch Eriboll, running out to sea at An t'Sron. However, this formation also makes up Ard Neackie, where limekilns reveal its presence, while it continues northwards as a thin strip along the coast towards the lighthouse at the mouth of Loch Eriboll. It can be examined on the slopes of Torr na Bithe, just to the north of the viewpoint itself, where it weathers out in the manner typical of limestone.

The Durness Limestone gives way to older rocks of the Cambrian sequence towards the east. Although the Pipe Rock is well-represented, the Fucoid Beds and Serpulite Grit are also present in some places, together with the Basal Quartzite. All these rocks are affected by folding and thrusting to such an extent that they are locally turned upside down. These structures are best seen around Ben Heilam, north of the main road. Traced to the south, all these rocks become hidden under the Lewisian Gneiss, where this formation is carried forward on the Arnaboll Thrust. This thrust reaches the coast just to the south of the viewpoint. However, it carries on its back not just Lewisian Gneiss but also Basal Quartzite and Pipe Rock at this point. The Basal Quartzite forms the conspicuous craigs overlooking the road just south of the viewpoint, while the Pipe Rock is exposed along the road at the back of Camas an Dun. All these rocks are slightly over-turned towards the northwest.

The Lewisian Gneiss lying on top of the Arnaboll Thrust overlooks much of the lower ground towards the head of Loch Eriboll. It makes the far crags of Beinn Arnaboll on the skyline to the southeast, lying beyond the exposures of Cambrian Quartzite just mentioned, while it also forms the prominent crags of Greag na Faoilinn, overlooking the head of Loch Eriboll. The original character of these gneisses has been destroyed in many places by the intensity of the earth-movements, converting them into flaggy and very fine-grained rocks known as mylonites.

All these rocks are capped by the Moine Thrust, which runs just below the skyline, east of Loch Eriboll. It does not make a very conspicuous feature in the landscape, although it brings forward the Moine Schists on top of the underlying rocks. The shallow southeasterly dip of the rocks lying above the Moine Thrust is clearly reflected in the slope of the skyline forming the summit of An Leancharn in the far distance.

LOCH ERIBOLL TO CAPE WRATH.

Continue west towards Durness along the A838 around the head of Loch Eriboll, where Creag na Faoilinn gives a much closer view of the Lewisian Gneiss, where it has been thrust over the underlying rocks. There is a wide terrace of fluvio-glacial gravels at the mouth of Strath Beag. Its surface is pock-marked by several lochans, which occupy "kettle-holes" where masses of "dead ice" have been left to melt away as the glaciers retreated at the end of the Last Glaciation. A stop can be made opposite **Polla** to take in the geological panorama up Strath Beag, where the effects of the Caledonian earth-movements are particularly clear.

Beyond this point, the road runs along the foot of the dip-slope formed by the Cambrian Quartzite where it is exposed to the northwest of Loch Eriboll. Beyond the turning to Portnancon, the road crosses a faulted contact made by these quartzites with the underlying gneisses, which form the higher ground around Beinn Ceannabeinne. The effects of glacial action are clearly seen 300 yards west of the road around [NC 440642], where there is a good example of a glacial pavement, and north of the side road leading to Rispond, where suberb examples of roches moutonnees can be seen around [NC 451656].

Just beyond the turning to Rispond, stop at the car-park overlooking the beach at **Ceannabeinne** [NC 443654]. The nearby exposures show banded gneisses (**MFG 254**), which are typical of the Lewisian Gneiss where it has been affected by the Laxfordian movements. Other good exposures are found at the western end of Ceannabeinne Beach [NC 441657], where darker layers of basic rock are present in the gneisses, breaking up into segments as the result of boudinage. Returning to the road, glacial striations are visible on a glacially-smoothed surface of Lewisian Gneiss which faces the road where it bends sharply to the right, some 200 yards west of the car-park. A perched block of Lewisian Gneiss, left behind by the ice when it melted away, makes a prominent feature after another 200 yards, just north of the road where it reaches the top of the hill.

LOCH ERIBOLL TO CAPE WRATH

The road then crosses a short stretch of country typical of the Lewisian Gneiss, before encountering Cambrian Quartzite and Pipe Rock around Sangobeg. The bedding shown by these quartzites can be seen in the low cliffs running out to sea at the next headland, just before Lerinmore is reached. These rocks are faulted against Durness Limestone, which is exposed at the roadside on approaching Smoo Cave [NC 419671].

The waters of the Allt Smoo now descend 70 feet into the **Smoo Cave** by disappearing down an impressive sink-hole, just south of the road. Over the years, this stream has dissolved away the limestone and dolomite to form the cave itself. It has much the largest entrance of any such cavern in Britain, 100 feet across and 50 feet high, and inside there is a second cave with an underground lake. Smoo Cave lies at the back of a long and narrow inlet of the sea, with very steep walls, forming a gorge-like feature. It seems likely that there was once a roof to this gorge, which then collapsed as the sea continued to pentrate inland along the line of the Allt Smoo.

Driving west along the A838 towards Sango Bay, more exposures of Durness Limestone are seen at the roadside. Sango Bay is underlain by shattered quartzites, schists and gneisses, lying on top of the Durness Limestone. The presence of these rocks might be thought a mystery until it is realised that they are an advance guard of the Moine Schists, thrust up the Moine Thrust high above the present level of erosion, and then dropped down by normal faulting at a much later date into their present position. As there are similar rocks at Faraid Head, some 10 miles across country from the line of the Moine Thrust itself at Loch Eriboll, the movements on this thrust-plane must have exceeded this figure. In fact, they were probably very much greater, as the rocks lying on top of the Moine Thrust have been thrust for many tens of miles across country from the east.

The normal faulting around Durness has preserved the Durness Limestone from the effects of erosion, well in advance of its main outcrop below the Moine Thrust at Loch Eriboll. One such fault is marked by the steep wall of Durness Limestone, which runs along the southeastern side of Sango Bay. It is this fault which brings down the metamorphic rocks to the northwest around the shores of this bay. There is another normal fault running southwest from Sangobeg. It crosses the low ground lying at the foot of the hills between the Kyle of Durness and Loch

JOHN O'GROATS TO CAPE WRATH

Eriboll. This fault throws Durness Limestone down to the northwest against Lewisian Gneiss to the southeast. The gneiss makes the higher ground to the southeast, capped by Cambrian Quartzite.

After passing through Durness, take the side road which leads to the ferry across the Kyle of Durness. Although this is just a passenger ferry (operating only in the summer months), it links up with a fast and furious minibus service to Cape Wrath. The route passes across the Lewisian Gneiss for most of the way, apart from an outlier of Cambrian Quartzite and Torridonian Sandstone around Daill. However, the hills to the north of the road are Torridonian Sandstone, faulted against Lewisian gneiss to the southwest, and capped with Cambrian Quartzite on Sgribhis-Bheinn. These hills reach the north coast at Clo Mor, where the Torridonian Sandstone is exposed in the highest cliffs on the British mainland, dropping over 900 feet into the sea, and stretching for nearly 2 miles along the coast. The hills south of the road are likewise Torridonian Sandstone, which also forms most of the coast-line south of Cape Wrath.

GEOLOGICAL VIEWPOINT: CAPE WRATH.

Although not so high as Clo Mor, the cliffs around Cape Wrath [NC 260747] rise to well over 400 feet, just east of the lighthouse. They provide spectacular views of the Lewisian Gneiss, showing that its banded nature is the result of alternations of light-coloured gneiss with much darker layers of basic rock, while the whole complex is cut by later sheets of granite and pegmatite. All these rocks are folded to a certain extent. There are good views out to sea, with the Butt of Lewis and North Rona visible on the far horizon.

HIGHLAND GEOLOGY TRAIL

CAPE WRATH TO ULLAPOOL.

South of Cape Wrath lie the Northwest Highlands, which acted as a foreland to the Caledonian earth-movements. This is classic ground, visited by generations of geologists, while even the casual tourist cannot fail to be impressed by how the geological foundations to the country are clothed in landscape and scenery.

The Northwest Highlands are bounded on the east by the Moine Thrust, which carries the Moine Schists of the Caledonian Highlands northwest over this ancient foreland. This great dislocation was accompanied by much folding and thrusting of the underlying rocks, along the south-eastern edge of the Northwest Highlands. These rocks now form a belt of structural complication, several miles in width, lying in advance of the Moine Trust itself. Apart from the Moine Thrust, several other thrusts are recognised as important elements of this thrust belt. They include the Glencoul, Ben More and Kishorn Thrusts, along with the Sole Thrust, below which the rocks lying farther to the northwest are not affected in any way by the Caledonian earth-movements.

The Northwest Highlands consist of Lewisian Gneiss, Torridonian Sandstone and Cambro-Ordovician rocks, and it is these rocks which are encountered within the Moine Thrust Belt, shuffled together by the Caledonian earth-movements. Farther northwest, they are not affected by these movements, and their original character can best be appreciated. The Lewisian Gneiss is exposed over wide areas as a very rough terrain of low rocky knolls and peaty hollows, strewn with a great many lochans. The Torridonian Sandstone gives rise to a quite different scenery of high mountains with many peaks, often rising abruptly in terraced slopes from a foundation of Lewisian Gneiss, and ringed around with great precipices. These mountains of dark-red sandstone are often capped by glistening white Cambrian Quartzite and Pipe Rock, which adds another distinctive feature to the landscape.

CAPE WRATH TO LAXFORD BRAE.

Returning from Cape Wrath across the Kyle of Durness, continue south along the A838 towards Scourie. The wide valley of the River Dionard is floored at first by the Durness Limestone, and typical exposures are seen where

49

the road crosses the river. The hills to the southeast are Lewisian Gneiss, capped at their very top by Cambrian Quartzite. Although Lewisian Gneiss also occurs northwest of the road, this gives way to Torridonian Sandstone as the road starts to climb towards Gualin House. It is this sandstone with its massive bedding which forms the slopes of Farrmheall, capped by Cambrian Quartzite.

Once Gualin House is reached, it can be seen just how rugged a terrain can be formed by Lewisian Gneiss, particularly where it makes the lower ground below Foinaven, southeast of the road. This makes a strong contrast with much more subdued topography to the northwest, which marks the outcrop of the Torridonian Sandstone with its lack of rocky exposure. The valley itself roughly follows the faulted contact separating these two geological formations from one another. Foinaven faces out northwest over this ground. Although its summit and eastern flanks are Cambrian Quartzite and Pipe Rock, its northernmost peak is Lewisian Gneiss. Its northwesterly slopes, like those of Carnstackie to the northeast and Arkle to the south, are all formed by Lewisian Gneiss. As the road descends towards the head of Loch Inchard at Rhiconich, it enters extremely craggy ground typical of the Lewisian Gneiss throughout the Northwest Highlands. Stop 2 miles south of Rhiconich in a layby at the locality now known as Laxford Brae.

GEOLOGICAL LOCALITY: LAXFORD BRAE.

The exposures along the road at this locality [NC 235901] provide an excellent section through the Lewisian Gneiss where it has been affected by the Laxfordian movements, showing the structural complexity typically displayed by these rocks. They are banded gneisses, intruded by much pegmatitic material, which forms the light-coloured masses of granitic rock, invading what must be older rocks in a very irregular fashion. The banded gneisses are themselves formed by alternations of different rock-types. The lighter layers are grey gneisses, approaching granite in composition if somewhat less acid, while the darker bands are much more basic rocks with the composition of basalt or gabbro.

Although the various layers in these banded gneisses often appear quite parallel to one another, careful examination shows that this is not always the case. In fact, a thin basic layer can be seen towards the northern end of the section, cutting across another basic layer at a slight angle (**MFG 253**). This means that two generations of basic rock are present within the Lewisian Gneiss at this locality. The cross-cutting layer may well represent the remnants of a Scourie Dyke, now almost incorporated into these Laxfordian Gneisses.

LAXFORD BRAE TO LOCH GLENCOUL.

Continue south towards Laxford Bridge, passing typical exposures of Lewisian Gneiss where the road reaches the shores of Loch Laxford. Turn left at Laxford Bridge along the A838 to make a detour to Loch Stack: otherwise turn right along the A894 towards Scourie. By parking at the southeastern end of **Loch Stack** around [NC 293416], a fine view can be obtained to the north, showing how the Cambrian Quartzite and Pipe Rock rests unconformably on top of Lewisian Gneiss along the southern flanks of Arkle. Like the bedding of the overlying sediments, this unconformity is inclined towards the southeast at a low angle. Traced down-dip in the same direction, it can be seen how these rocks get caught up by the Caledonian earth-movements, so that they become increasingly disturbed in this direction. Return to Laxford Bridge and continue west along the A894 towards Scourie.

The road from Laxford Bridge to Scourie crosses the geological boundary separating the Scourian and Laxfordian elements within the Lewisian complex as a whole. It is marked by a wide zone of granitic sheets, which runs northwest-southeast along both shores of Loch Laxford. The much older Scourian Gneisses lie beyond this zone to the southwest, where they can be seen around Scourie.

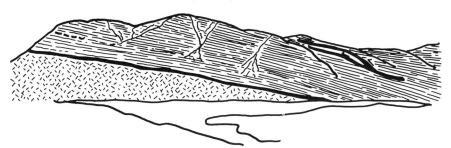

Figure 7. The Unconformity on Arkle.

CAPE WRATH TO ULLAPOOL

Even the casual visitor can appreciate this change in the geology since the Scourian Gneisses lack much in the way of granite, unlike the Lewisian Gneisses of Laxfordian age to the northeast. This gives a rather gloomy feel to the landscape around Scourie and farther south, often marked by drab outcrops of rather dark rock, particularly in the deep roadcuts along the A894. Farther north, the landscape feels more cheerful as there is much granite, forming light-coloured exposures glinting in the sun.

Two coastal sections can be recommended to the visitor who wants to get to grips with the geological complexities of the Lewisian Gneiss. The first lies north of **Tarbet** [NC 489163], where the Scourian Gneisses give way to the Laxfordian rocks across what is known as the Laxford Front, itself marked by the zone of granite sheets along Loch Laxford. The second lies south of Scourie, where a Scourie Dyke is exposed on the coast around [NC 145415] near **Upper Badcall,** cutting across Scourian Gneisses where they are little affected by the Laxfordian movements. Both localities are fully described in the Geologists' Association Guide to the Lewisian and Torridonian Rocks of the North-West Highlands, which can be obtained at local bookshops.

Driving south along the A894 from Scourie, Quinag comes into view, just before Kylesku. This mountain is nearly all Torridonian Sandstone, magnificently exposed in the great buttresses of Sail Gorm and Sail Garbh, which face out over the Lewisian Gneiss to the north. However, there is a capping of Cambrian Quartzite on its highest summit, while this quartzite also forms a great sheet which descends its eastern flanks from Spidean Coinich. The unconformity which separates these Cambrian rocks from the underlying Torridonian Sandstone can be seen from certain viewpoints. After crossing the bridge at Kylesku, stop after nearly 2 miles at a layby on the left just beyond Unapool House [NC 233316].

GEOLOGICAL VIEWPOINT: LOCH GLENCOUL.

Looking east from this point provides quite the best view of a thrust fault anywhere in the British Isles. It is known as the Glencoul Thrust (**MFG 147**), and it affects the rocks lying underneath the Moine Thrust. This thrust is exposed on the western slopes of Beinn Aird na Loch, which is the hill with a rather broad top, lying to the east across Loch Glencoul. Its western slopes, around the promontory of Aird na Loch, consist of very rough but rather featureless ground, typical as always of the Lewisian Gneiss. These slopes lie below a very prominent line of crags which can be traced down the hillside towards the right. These crags are formed by the Cambrian Quartzite and Pipe Rock, dipping at a low angle towards the east, and lying unconformably on top of the Lewisian Gneiss to the west. The bedding of these sedimentary rocks can easily be seen, even at a distance. These crags form an escarpment, backed by a sloping shelf that runs down to the shore of Loch Glencoul. This is a dip-slope and its eastern edge marks the outcrop of the Fucoid Beds, which are found immediately underneath the Glencoul Thrust. This plane of movement carries Lewisian Gneiss on its back, so that this formation is also exposed in typical fashion on the upper slopes of Beinn Aird na Loch to the east.

The presence of the Glencoul Thrust is clearly reflected in the topography, which shows how the Cambrian rocks are sandwiched between Lewisian Gneiss. Evidently, the Lewisian Gneiss lying on top of the Cambrian rocks has been thrust up and over these rocks from the east, probably by several miles at the very least. The Lewisian Gneiss forming the upper slopes of Beinn Aird na Loch above the Glencoul Thrust can be traced for more than 2 miles to the east towards the outcrop of the Moine Thrust at the head of Glencoul. This thrust is exposed on the Stack of Glencoul, which makes a prominent feature on the eastern skyline. It brings Moine Schists forward from the east over Cambrian Quartzite and Pipe Rock, which lies unconformably on top of the Lewisian Gneiss above the Glencoul Thrust.

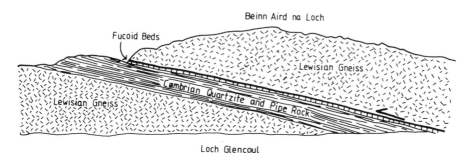

Figure 8. The Glencoul Thrust.

GEOLOGICAL LOCALITY: LOCH GLENCOUL.

A splendid exposure of the Glencoul Thrust can be visited by driving another mile along the A894 towards Skiag Bridge. After parking just after the road crosses a bridge [NC 236303], walk east along the junction which marks the unconformity between grey Lewisian Gneiss to the north and chocolate-coloured Torridonian Sandstone to the south. After a short distance, a backward view reveals the line of this unconformity as it rises to a height of 1000 feet at the foot of Sail Garbh. Skirting round the hillside, the Cambrian Quartzite is next encountered, cutting down to the east across the Torridonian Sandstone until it comes to rest on Lewisian Gneiss at [NC 245302]. This marks the position of the double unconformity between Lewisian Gneiss, Torridonian Sandstone and Cambrian Quartzite, which is such a characteristic feature of this ground. Looking back, the eye can follow the base of the Cambrian Quartzite straight to the top of Sail Garbh.

Continue down the slope around the foot of a broken escarpment, picked out by a line of small trees, at the back of Liath Bhad, where the Fucoid Beds are exposed in typical fashion. After crossing the ground to the east, scramble up a steep slope to the foot of the rocky craigs which overlook Loch Glencoul at this point [NC 259302]. These craigs are formed by Lewisian Gneiss, broken down along the line of the Glencoul Thrust into dull and very dark rocks with a platy structure. These rocks form an overhang, below which creamy-coloured dolomites of the Durness Limestone are found. There is a clean-cut line between broken-down gneiss and the underlying dolomite, which marks the plane of the Glencoul Thrust (**MFG 148**).

UNAPOOL TO CLACHTOLL.

Returning to the main road, there is a choice of routes that can be taken to reach Clachtoll. The more direct route continues along the A894 to Skiag Bridge, where the A837 can be followed towards Lochinver. On reaching the outskirts of this village, turn right along the B869 towards Clachtoll, and stop in the car-park, just west of the road at [NC 039272]. However, as the trail follows this route at a later stage, the longer and much slower road through Drumbeg can be taken as a more scenic alternative. This road joins the A894 near Unapool as the B869. It crosses low-lying but very rough country typical of the Lewisian Gneiss along most of its course. However,

south of Clashnessie Bay, it runs along the contact between these gneisses and Torridonian Sandstone. Stop in
the car-park near the beach at Clachtoll [NC 039272].

GEOLOGICAL LOCALITY: CLACHTOLL.

The unconformity between the Torridonian sandstones of
the older Stoer Group and the underlying Lewisian Gneiss
can first be examined in the crags just east of the road.
Cross the road from the car-park, and walk up a track
past a small quarry. This exposes red Torridonian mudstones with well-marked jointing, which pass downwards
into well-bedded grits and breccias to the east. After
passing a cottage, climb up a broad gully to the top of a
small hill overlooking the car-park. Its top is formed by a
glacial pavement, exposing coarse breccias with many
fragments of acid gneiss, together with scattered blocks
of a dark ultrabasic rock. Behind this hill is a ruined
croft [NC 043272], and the unconformity can be located
just a few yards to its west, where coarse breccias rest
directly on top of the Lewisian Gneiss. The unconformity
can then be followed south towards the road, although it
is nowhere exposed, separating breccias to the west from
gneisses to the east.

Cross the road, and walk south across the fields, keeping
well to the left of the jagged rocks guarding the entrance
to Clachtoll Bay. A faulted contact between Torridonian
Sandstone and the underlying gneiss is hidden by sand at
a small inlet on the south coast at [NC 039268]. The
Lewisian Gneiss forming the rock-face immediately east
of this inlet is cut by a series of Neptunian dykes (**MFG
104**), filled with chocolate-coloured mudstone. These
fissures opened up in Torridonian times, allowing sediment
to be washed in from the surface. Angular fragments of
the gneiss, broken off the walls, lie surrounded by mudstone in some places, and locally the rock passes into a
breccia. Beyond these exposures to the southeast, There is
a tongue of Torridonian breccia, just above high-water
mark, plastered against a cliff of Lewisian Gneiss.

Returning to the sandy inlet, red mudstones are exposed
to the west beyond the Lewisian Gneiss. Occasional beds
of gritty sandstone are present in these mudstones, and
the lowermost sandstone is cut by two sets of thrust-
faults, dipping at low angles towards one another. The
mudstones are cut by a complex network of very closely-
spaced joints, which obscures the bedding in these rocks.

Walking back around the coast towards Clachtoll, the unconformity can be located again just before the path descends to the beach at [NC 040270]. The Torridonian rocks of the headland are cut off by a fault, which brings up Lewisian Gneiss so that it is exposed along the coast just southwest of the beach. The banding of this gneiss dips steeply towards the southwest. Mudstones can be seen resting against this gneiss just to its northeast, forming a near-vertical unconformity, along which a thin breccia is found. This contact follows the banding in the gneiss, and evidently formed a low cliff, against which the Torridonian rocks were deposited.

Walk northwest around the Bay of Clachtoll to the west coast just south of Sgeir na Traghad at [NC 036274]. The mudstones exposed around the Bay of Clachtoll give way to cross-bedded sandstones in this direction, forming slightly higher ground to the west. These sandstones are extremely well-exposed along the west coast, where they occur as thick beds separated from one another by shales and mudstones. Dipping out to sea at 30 degrees, there is one bedding-plane, exposed over a very wide area. It is crossed by the trace of a normal fault, which forms an irregular step in the bedding (**MFG 124**).

CLACHTOLL TO ENARD BAY.

Return to the car park, and drive southeast towards Lochinver along the B869 across a rocky landscape, typical of the Lewisian Gneiss. The Ordnance Survey Map (Sheet 15) shows that the road runs along a narrow steep-sided valley, which can be traced towards the southeast from Maiden Loch, past Rhicarn and Brackloch, and across the River Inver. This feature marks the trace of an ultrabasic dyke, which is particularly susceptible to weathering and erosion. There are many such features cutting across the Lewisian Gneiss in this direction, imparting a pronounced grain to the country. After driving up the steep hill near Polla, stop at its summit [NC 075257], where there is a fine view of Suilven, Canisp and Cul Mor, rising abruptly as isolated relics of Torridonian Sandstone above a low-lying but very rough platform of Lewisian Gneiss. The view is even better from the slightly higher ground just north of the road.

On reaching the A837, turn right and drive through Lochinver. Take the unclassified road that leads south past the school towards Inverkirkaig and beyond. The

GEOLOGICAL LOCALITY: ENARD BAY

twists and turns of this single-track road are typical of the country formed by the Lewisian Gneiss, which may be examined almost anywhere along its course. After crossing the River Polly, the road eventually passes from Lewisian Gneiss on to Torridonian Sandstone as it climbs over the Aird of Coigach. There is an abrupt change in topography as the extremely rough country of rocky knolls, lochans and peaty hollows, which is characteristic of the Lewisian Gneiss, gives way to rolling moorlands covered with peat, formed by the Torridonian Sandstone with its mantle of boulder clay on the lower ground. There is a fine view from the summit of this hill [NC 074115], dominated by the sharp peak of Stac Pollaidh just to the east. All the mountains are Torridonian Sandstone, ranging from Ben More Coigach to the southeast, Cul Mor to the east, and Suilven and Canisp to the northeast. On reaching Loch Bad a'Ghail, turn right towards Achiltibuie, and park at a bend in the road at [NC 025127].

GEOLOGICAL LOCALITY: ENARD BAY.

Walk north over easy ground towards the coast east of Achnahaird Bay. A rocky knoll, scoured smooth by the ice, exposes Lewisian Gneiss surrounded by Torridonian Sandstone at [NC 023135]. Farther on, coastal exposures around [NC 022143] consist of red Torridonian sandstones with cross-bedding in large units, up to 12 feet thick. The internal bedding within these cross-bedded units is very well-exposed as curving surfaces, dipping more steeply that the bedding itself. The currents depositing these sandstones evidently flowed from the northeast. Farther north, beyond a small bay, which marks the trace of a fault, climb over the shoulder of Cnoc Mor an Rubha Bhig to reach the north coast at a narrow inlet [NC 027143]. This inlet lies below a steep slope of Torridonian Sandstone belonging to the Stoer Group, down which a sheep track can be followed to the shore.

These sandstones are exposed as a slight overhang along the western wall of the inlet. Dipping moderately towards the west, they rest with an erosive contact on top of red mudstones at the back of the inlet. These mudstones are very much jointed and fractured. They become gritty as they are traced to the east, where they pass over a distance of a few yards into a gneiss breccia. Walk to the seaward end of a slight promontory which lies just east of this inlet, where these breccias are best exposed, facing out to sea. These breccias are banked against a

57

hill of Lewisian Gneiss which forms the promontory itself. The contact is close to the vertical along its western side. More breccias are found around the eastern side of this promontory, passing into gritty mudstones, banked against the Lewisian Gneiss. All these exposures lie to the west of an almost enclosed bay, which can be identified by the ruins of a bothy at [NC 028146].

Walk around the shores of this bay past the ruined bothy to the next headland, passing exposures of Torridonian conglomerate. The seaward end of this headland is formed by another hill of Lewisian Gneiss, mantled by coarse breccias carrying angular fragments of the underlying gneiss. These breccias are well-exposed along the western side of the headland. They can be traced eastwards across a narrow neck of land where the sea has almost cut off this headland, about 100 yards north of the bothy. There, the gneiss breccia has a matrix of fine-grained limestone, which weathers away to form a fretted surface, typical of calcareous rocks. The breccia then passes up into a thin horizon of finely-laminated limestone at its very top, carrying scattered blocks of gneiss. This limestone underlies a few feet of red mudstones, forming an easily-eroded horizon that has been penetrated to some extent by the sea. All these rocks form a mound, over which Torridonian conglomerate appears draped to the south. This conglomerate is quite unlike the underlying breccias of Lewisian Gneiss because it carries large boulders of sandstone, thought to be derived from the sandstone outcrop just to the west.

This sandstone conglomerate is exposed along the coast towards the east, while its base can be traced inland to where it reaches the coast again, just west of the next bay to the east [NC 030147]. There, the conglomerate is underlain by red mudstones, which carry thin beds of gritty limestone. The contact has been undercut by the sea. The mudstones pass down into drab red sandstones, which form slabby exposures on the foreshore. At a slight headland, 100 yards to the east of this contact, careful search will reveal accretionary lapilli as pea-sized nodules, exposed on the bedding. These are thought to be fossil rain-drops, formed by the accretion of volcanic dust in the rain-clouds that accompany volcanic eruptions. Walk south to the road from this point, over ground which provides excellent views of the Torridonian mountains towards the east beyond the shores of Enard Bay.

GEOLOGICAL LOCALITY: LOCH ASSYNT

Return to Lochinver, and continue east along the A837 towards Skiag Bridge. The road crosses Lewisian Gneiss for much of this distance, but Torridonian Sandstone is exposed to the east, where it forms the precipitous slopes of Quinag. The unconformity can itself be traced from a height of nearly 2000 feet below the northern face of Sail Gorm, down to the shores of Loch Assynt, where it is exposed along the road about 2½ miles east of Loch-assynt Lodge. Park where a straight stretch of road runs along the shore of Loch Assynt, 200 yards beyond some small islands with scattered pine-trees.

GEOLOGICAL LOCALITY: LOCH ASSYNT.

The roadside exposures at [NC 217251] clearly show the basal beds of the Torridonian Sandstone where they rest unconformably on top of the Lewisian Gneiss. The gneiss forms the greyish and rather blocky rocks, exposed just above the road. Although rather massive in appearance, they are banded rocks, dipping moderately steeply towards the west. They are capped by dark red sandstones and shales, carrying pebbles of vein quartz, which are the well-bedded rocks exposed towards the top of the cutting. These are Torridonian in age, and the intervening surface of unconformity represents a gap in geological time of some 600 million years at the very least.

Continue east along the road towards Skiag Bridge, which crosses from Torridonian Sandstone on to Cambrian Quartzite at the back of a shallow valley after less than a mile from the previous locality. The Cambrian Quartzite makes a prominent escarpment, overlooking this valley, which can be traced up the slopes of Quinag towards the west. There is a marked contrast in colour between the dark Torridonian Sandstones and the light-coloured Cambrian Quartzites. After passing roadside exposures of Cambrian Quartzite, park as convenient near Skiag Bridge [NC 234244].

GEOLOGICAL EXCURSION: SKIAG BRIDGE.

A short walk from Skiag Bridge, over fairly rough ground, serves to illustrate many features of the local geology. First return back along the A837 to the bend in the road at [NC 231245]. The roadcut to the north exposes typical cross-bedded Cambrian quartzites with some gritty layers. These rocks dip to the east at 10 degrees. These rocks are overlain by Pipe Rock, which is poorly exposed some 20 yards north of the road.

The view east from this point clearly shows the sedimentary sequence displayed by the Cambro-Ordovician rocks. The Pipe Rock outcrops downhill as far as Skiag Bridge, where it is well-exposed in the steep face above the road. On top of this formation are the Fucoid beds, which make the brown-weathering exposures on the hillside just above the Pipe Rock. The slight hollow running downhill towards the AA box marks the more shaly horizons that are present towards the top of the Fucoid Beds. These rocks are succeeded by the Serpulite Grit, which makes a prominent line of craigs that runs down to a promontory, jutting out into Loch Assynt opposite Ardveck Castle.

Above this escarpment, there is a sharp break in slope, beyond which the Durness Limestone is exposed. Its outcrop is marked by grassy slopes, quite unlike the much wetter ground formed by the underlying rocks, covered with heather and bracken. The higher ground beyond the Durness Limestone is formed by Lewisian Gneiss, together with Cambrian Quartzite and Pipe Rock, carried forward over the underlying rocks to the west by the Glencoul Thrust. These rocks make the rocky slopes of Glas Beinn and Cnoc na Creige, lying just east of the A894 road.

Now walk uphill towards the northwest along the top of the quartzite escarpment. Crossing the stream draining from Lochan Feoir, make for a slight col at the eastern end of Lochan an Duibhe. The rocks exposed just uphill from this point [NC 223256] are pebbly Torridonian sandstones, with the bedding picked out by lines of pebbles, mostly vein quartz. The sandstone is rich in felspar, which gives the rock its pink colour. Overlying these rocks are Cambrian quartzites, exposed farther up the slope.

Walk around this slope to the north, underneath some craigs of Cambrian Quartzite, and the unconformity can be located at [NC 221258], some 150 yards north of north-east of the lochan. There, dark Torridonian sandstones are overlain by light-coloured Cambrian quartzite, dipping more steeply to the east than the underlying rocks, which are flat-lying. There is a thin pebbly grit with detrital feldspar at the base of the Cambrian sequence.

This locality provides a fine view of the double unconformity on the slopes of Beinn Garbh, beyond Loch Assynt to the south. The lower slopes of this hill are formed by rocky knolls of Lewisian Gneiss. Uphill, the slopes become steeper, and they are terraced in the manner typical of the Torridonian Sandstone. Although the Torridonian Sandstone is close to the horizontal, this formation rests unconformably on Lewisian Gneiss, burying what was once an ancient landscape of low hills and shallow valleys. The slopes of Beinn Garbh to the east are Cambrian Quartzite, dipping in the same direction at an angle close to the slope of the hillside. The quartzite cuts across the bedding of the Torridonian Sandstone towards the east, eventually coming to rest on the Lewisian Gneiiss. Clearly, the Torridonian Sandstone was tilted towards the west, prior to the deposition of the Cambrian rocks. These rocks were most likely deposited very close to the horizontal on what was a plane of marine erosion, so that they stepped across from Lewisian Gneiss in the east on to Torridonian Sandstone in the west. The Torridonian Sandstone was then tilted back towards the east, along with the overlying Cambrian rocks, so that it has now regained its original attitude, while the Cambrian rocks have come to dip towards the east.

Walking back east from this point, keep well up the slope until a path is reached north of Lochan Feoir. This leads to the wide dip-slope formed by the Cambrian Quartzite and Pipe Rock, west of Allt Sgaithaigh. Walk east over rough ground to reach this stream around [NC 230255], where it runs over a series of bedding-planes in the Pipe Rock. Excellent sections show large "Trumpet Pipes" at this locality, showing up as large circular depressions, up to 4 inches across with a slightly raised centre, packed closely together on the bedding-surfaces. Continue east to the A894, and walk down this road to Skiag Bridge.

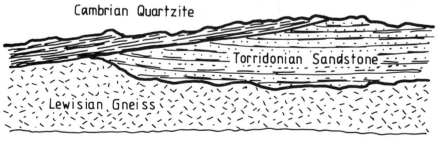

Figure 9. The double unconformity on Beinn Garbh.

CAPE WRATH TO ULLAPOOL

This road follows the contact between the Pipe Rock and the Fucoid Beds towards Skiag Bridge. After passing exposures of the Fucoid Beds, the Pipe Rock can be examined in the steep rock-face, close to the road junction. It consists of purplish and white quartzites, cross-bedded in places and cut by a multitude of vertical pipes, up to 18 inches in length and filled with much whiter quartzite. These pipes are the traces of worm-burrows, filled with fine sand. They give a typically pitted appearance to the bedding-surfaces, which often allows the Pipe Rock to be recognised in the field.

The contact between the Pipe Rock and the overlying Fucoid Beds can be found by walking 200 yards east along the A837 towards Inchnadamph. Unlike the light-coloured quartzites forming the uppermost beds of Pipe Rock, the Fucoid Beds are brown-weathering sandy dolomites, with rather irregular bedding and much shaly material. The lowermost beds of this formation are seen at the roadside, while there are also good exposures along the shore of Loch Assynt, opposite the AA box. Careful examination of the bedding-planes exposed below the road may reveal worm-like traces, up to half an inch across, which are the flattened remains of organic burrows, filled with sand. It was these markings that the early geologists thought were made by seaweed, so accounting for the name given to these beds. The uppermost horizons of the Fucoid Beds are mostly shales, which outcrop along the hollow which runs uphill from the AA box, just to the west of the crag formed by the Serpulite Grit.

The Serpulite Grit can next be examined along the roadside to the east of the AA box, where it forms a gritty quartzite, often somewhat calcareous to judge by its weathering. It resembles the underlying Pipe Rock in that worm burrows are present as vertical pipes, filled with sand. The fossil that gives this horizon its name is now known as Salterella. It is preserved in profusion on some bedding-planes, where it forms conical, worm-like impressions, up to a quarter inch in length. It is best seen where the Serpulite Grit reaches Loch Assynt in a low promontory, across the bay from Ardvreck Castle.

Return to the road where the lowermost beds of the Durness Limestone are seen to rest abruptly on top of the Serpulite Grit, some 50 yards to the east of the AA box. These dark limestones share the same easterly dip as the underlying rocks. However, walking along the road to the east reveals that a sudden change in dip at the back of the small bay, north of Ardvreck Castle. This marks the trace of the lowermost thrust to affect the rocks of the Assynt region, well in advance of the Moine Thrust, which lies several miles farther east at this point.

SKIAG BRIDGE TO KNOCKAN CLIFF.

The route south from Skiag Bridge along the A837 runs past Inchnadamph along the valley of the River Loanan. It follows the outcrop of the lowermost thrusts to affect the Moine Thrust Belt to the east. The Sole Thrust itself occurs within the Fucoid Beds along most of its course, although it occasionally rises into the Durness Limestone, close to its base. The Basal Quartzite and Pipe Rock are therefore not affected by the thrusting. They are exposed west of the road in very long dip-slopes, descending east from the summits of Beinn Garbh, Canisp, and Cul Mor. The Cambrian Quartzite and Pipe Rock are highly imper- meable rocks, giving very marshy ground covered in peat and heather, while the Durness Limestone to the east often weathers into a good soil, covered with grass. Just before Inchnadamph, the A837 passes a memorial to Peach and Horne, who mapped this ground, and indeed much of the Northwest Highlands, for the Geological Survey of Scotland during the final decades of the 19th century. It lies west of the road at the top of a small hill.

A short walk up the valley of the **River Traligill** from Inchnadamph provides an excellent view of a thrust-plane, where it is exposed in the river-bed at [NC 267212], southeast of Glenbain Cottage. Upstream, the river runs below ground for a quarter of a mile, and the best expo- sure of the thrust-plane is found where it reappears at the surface. Such underground drainage is typical of rivers in limestone terrain, where the solid rock can be dissol- ved away by slightly acid waters.

Just south of Inchnadamph, the road runs for well over a mile below the escarpment of Stronrubie, formed by the Durness Limestone. Beyond this point, however, there is little of geological interest until the hills of Cnoc an Leathaid come into view, west of Loch Awe. The Sole Thrust advances to the west at this point, carrying for- ward Lewisian Gneiss which, with its cover of Cambrian Quartzite and Pipe Rock, makes the summits of these two hills. East of the road, the upper slopes of Beinn nan Cnaimhseag and Beinn an Fhuarain expose Torridonian

63

CAPE WRATH TO ULLAPOOL

Sandstone, thrust westwards over the underlying Durness Limestone on the Ben More Thrust.

Turn right at Ledmore along the A835 towards Elphin, where the Durness Limestone is thrust over the Fucoid Beds and Serpulite Grit. The limestone is well-exposed in the cliffs overlooking the village. After crossing the Durness Limestone, the road passes over Serpulite Grit and the Fucoid Beds as it ascends the hill to the south. Just beyond the cairn marking the boundary of the Inverpolly Nature Reserve, turn left into the car-park at the foot of Knockan Cliff [NC 188091].

GEOLOGICAL LOCALITY: KNOCKAN CLIFF.

Knockan Cliff is a National Nature Reserve, so declared for its geological importance by the Nature Conservancy Council. It provides quite the best exposure of the Moine Thrust anywhere in the Northwest Highlands. The car-park looks out over a dip-slope of Cambrian Quartzite, descending towards the road from the slopes of Cul Mor to the northwest. Beyond lies a terraced landscape of Torridonian Sandstone, building the nearby mountains of Cul Mor and Cul Beag, while Stac Pollaidh is seen on the far skyline, beyond Gleann Laoigh.

Walk up the path from the car-park, passing the Pipe Rock in the quarry to the left, and then crossing the Fucoid Beds and the Serpulite Grit as the path climbs up the hillside. Just below the dark crags at the top of this slope, creamy-white dolomites are exposed, marking the outcrop of the Durness Limestone. These dolomites are separated from the rocks below by the Sole Thrust, which is not exposed. There is then an abrupt contact between these dolomites and much darker rocks which make the cliffs at the top of the slope. These dark rocks are the Moine Schists, and their abrupt contact with the underlying rocks is the line of the Moine Thrust (**MFG 149**).

This thrust can be traced for some 200 yards along the face of the cliff, everywhere forming a sharp break between the light-coloured dolomites and the much darker schists. In some places, the weathering of the dolomite has produced an overhang along this contact, where it can be seen that the Moine Thrust is inclined towards the east at quite a low angle, 10 degrees at the very most. The rocks lying just above the Moine Thrust are not typical of the Moine Schists as a whole. The vast movements on this thrust-plane have reduced these schists to what

64

are mylonites all along its course, breaking down and drawing out the original constituents in the rock.

On reaching the top of the slope north of Knockan Cliff, walk northeast for nearly a mile over Durness Limestone to an excellent viewpoint above Elphin. The Torridonian mountains of Suiven and Canisp are conspicuous to the north, capped by Cambrian Quartzite on Canisp. Quartzite and Pipe Rock then form a long dip-slope, descending towards the east. It ends in the outcrop of the Sole Thrust, following the Fucoid Beds or Durness Limestone, along the lower ground towards Inchnadamph, as already described. The thrust mass of Lewisian Gneiss, capped by Cambrian rocks, forms the prominent hills of Cnoc an Leathaid, just north of Cam Loch. Farther east, Torridonian Sandstone forms an isolated mass on Beinn an Fhuarain, thrust over the underlying Durness Limestone. Cnoc na Sroine above Loch Borolan is syenite, forming an igneous intrusion into the surrounding rocks. The higher and more distant hills on the skyline to the northeast, including Sgonnan Mhor and Ben More Assynt, are mostly Lewisian Gneiss, thrust together with Cambrian Quartzite and Pipe Rock over the underlying rocks to the west. The Moine thrust does not appear at all in this view, since it makes a wide detour away from its normal course, northeast of Knockan Cliff,, eventually passing to the east of Ben More Assynt. Only north of the Stack of Glencoul does it regain its original course. Return to the car-park from the view-point, by the same route, avoiding the steep slopes above the road.

KNOCKAN CLIFF TO ULLAPOOL.

Continue south along the A835 towards Ullapool, following the Moine Thrust for most of the way. The many cuttings along this road expose flaggy mylonites at first. However, south of the road junction to Achiltibuie, there are exposures of Cambrian Quartzite and Pipe Rock along the road, while Ben More Coigach makes the prominent mountain of Torridonian Sandstone to the west. After crossing Strath Kanaird, the road runs along a narrow valley, eroded along the line of a fault. It separates Cambrian Quartzite to the northwest from Torridonian Sandstone to the southeast. The quartzites in particular have been shattered by the faulting. The road then crosses Torridonian Sandstone, exposed in typical fashion, before it enters Ullapool. This village is built upon a wide terrace of superficial deposits, extending out into Loch Broom.

65

HIGHLAND GEOLOGY TRAIL

ULLLAPOOL TO KYLE OF LOCHALSH.

The geology does not change greatly south of Ullapool, as all the features recognised farther north can be traced from Assynt into Wester Ross. The Moine Thrust and its belt of structural complications continue towards the south, while the Moine Schists are exposed widely in the ground farther to the east. Northwest of the Moine Thrust lie the Lewisian Gneiss, Torridonian Sandstone and Cambro-Ordovician rocks of the Caledonian foreland, where the earth-movements affecting the Moine Schists had little or no effect.

Again, the foundations of geology determine the nature of the landscape. The Lewisian Gneiss is far more restricted in its outcrop, so that the extremely rough terrain typical of these rocks in the Northwest Highlands is absent farther south, except locally around Gairloch and Torridon. The Torridonian Sandstone outcrops much more widely, exposed in a magnificent series of real mountains with great corries and ridges, like An Teallach, Beinn Eighe, Liathach, and the Applecross hills, quite unlike the Torridonian hills farther north. Equally, the Moine Thrust does not make such a prominent feature in the landscape, except locally, as it does not carry forward the great masses of Lewisian Gneiss, which make the mountains like Ben More Assynt along its course farther to the north.

ULLAPOOL TO DUNDONELL.

Starting at Ullapool, drive east along the A835 towards the head of Loch Broom. The road passes over Torridonian Sandstone on to Cambrian Quartzite and Pipe Rock, after which the Fucoid Beds are encountered, weathering rusty-brown in typical fashion. The road then crosses the Sole Thrust, exposed just east of a bridge, 1½ miles from Ullapool. Torridonian Sandstone and Cambrian Quartzite are thrust over Durness Limestone. Just after the road returns to the coast beyond Corrie Point, mylonites (**MFG 131**) are exposed in a series of roadcuts. These are very black and extremely fine-grained rocks, in which folding can be seen where it affects very thin but continuous bands of lighter-coloured rock. These intensely deformed rocks, lacking any trace of original character, occur just above the Moine Thrust at this locality.

ULLAPOOL TO DUNDONELL

The trace of this thrust can be seen across Loch Broom, where it follows the break between the craggy ground underlain by Torridonian Sandstone (and Lewisian Gneiss) to the west, and the much smoother terrain to the east. Continuing towards the head of Loch Broom, the Moine Schists lying above this thrust are clearly exposed on the hillsides above Loch Broom, mostly dipping at a gentle angle towards the east. These rocks are also seen in a series of roadside exposures after passing the head of Loch Broom. Stop in the car-park for Corrieshalloch Gorge, a mile beyond Braemore.

Corrieshalloch Gorge is a very deep but narrow gorge, eroded by the melt waters of the glaciers as they retreated at the end of the Great Ice Age. The view from the suspension bridge over the Falls of Measach shows flat-lying Moine Schists, cut by very prominent joints in a northwesterly direction. These joints evidently acted as planes of weakness, along which the gorge itself was formed by erosion. It is nearly a mile long, and 200 feet deep. The vertical walls follow the joint-planes in the rock. Although the surrounding landscape is obscured by trees, the gorge lies just northwest of a broad valley, where the waters of the Abhainn Droma flow across what evidently was once a watershed, now breached by glacial action.

Return to the car-park, continue east along the A835 for half a mile, and then turn right at the road junction along the A832 towards Dundonell. The route first passes over Moine Schists for several miles. Crossing the high ground towards Dundonell, there are excellent views northwest towards An Teallach. Descending towards the north, the road enters the deep valley of the Dundonell River, overlooked on its east by steep crags of Moine Schists.

The road crosses the Moine Thrust at the mouth of this valley, where it opens out into Strath Beag. The dip-slope facing the road at this point is Cambrian Quartzite, which makes a very pronounced feature running across the southeastern slopes of An Teallach. Cambrian Quartzite also occurs as outliers on the An Teallach ridge and its eastern spurs, capping the tops of Sial Liath, Glas Mheall Liath and Glas Mheall Mor. The quartzite rests unconformably on Torridonian Sandstone, making up the other summits of An Teallach, and magnificently exposed in the precipices of its eastern corries.

ULLAPOOL TO KYLE OF LOCHALSH

Stop at a layby [NH 108868], half a mile to the north of **Dundonell House.** The view east shows a cross-section through the Moine Thrust. Creag Chorcurach is Moine Schist, resting on top of the thrust, which lies hidden under the screes lower down the slope. The rocks below the thrust are Cambrian Quartzite, forming the low crags farther to the west. Beyond, Torridonian Sandstone makes the lower ground before rising towards the summit of Beinn nam Ban.

DUNDONELL TO LOCH MAREE.

The road continues northwest from Dundonell along the shores of Little Loch Broom, passing through a landscape typical of the Torridonian Sandstone until it reaches Mungasdale on the eastern shore of Gruinard Bay. There is then an abrupt change in topography as the unconformity is crossed between the Torridonian Sandstone and the underlying Lewisian Gneiss. The gneiss is exposed in a great many rocky knolls and crags, separated from one another by steep-sided valleys. Typical exposures are seen west of the Little Gruinard River where the road climbs a steep hill to the viewpoint at [NH 940901]. The Lewisian Gneiss at this point forms an intimate mixture of acid and basic gneiss, where veins of light-coloured granite have invaded the much darker basic gneisses in a very irregular manner.

Beyond this point, the road crosses back on to the Torridonian Sandstone, which makes the much low ground mantled with boulder clay around the shores of Loch Ewe. Lewisian Gneiss is encountered once more just beyond Poolewe, where it is brought to the surface by a fault that runs northwest from Loch Maree along the course of the River Ewe. On crossing this river at Poolewe, there is a wide and very flat terrace of fluvio-glacial deposits around Pool Crofts. This is backed by high ground where the Lewisian Gneiss is exposed in an escarpment which follows the line of the Loch Maree Fault. Just over a mile south of Poolewe, there is an excellent view from the road towards Loch Maree, looking southeast from the viewpoint above Tollie Farm. The road then continues across Lewisian Gneiss towards Gairloch, where the Torridonian Sandstone reaches the coast. The village is built on another terrace at a height of some 50 feet above sea-level.

68

GEOLOGICAL PANORAMA: LOCH MAREE

Continue south from Gairloch along the A832, crossing over Lewisian Gneiss until the shores of Loch Maree are reached around Talladale. The Torridonian Sandstone is encountered once more beyond this point, as shown by the terraced nature of the hillsides. Good exposures are seen along the road. Looking across Loch Maree, it can be seen that Lewisian Gneiss outcrops along its northeastern shore, which follows the straight northwesterly trend of the Loch Maree Fault. Park at the layby [NG 982670], just over a mile past the Bridge of Grudie.

GEOLOGICAL PANORAMA: LOCH MAREE.

The well-known view across Loch Maree from this point shows the shapely peak of Slioch, rising steeply to the northeast. Its foundations are Lewisian Gneiss, which can be identified even at a distance by the silvery-grey outcrops on the lower slopes of this mountain. The gneiss is covered unconformably by well-bedded Torridonian Sandstone, typically dark-purple in colour, making the upper ramparts of this mountain. This unconformity represents a very ancient land-surface of hills and valleys in the Lewisian Gneiss, which were subsequently buried underneath the Torridonian Sandstone. This is well seen around Meall Riabhach, where the Lewisian Gneiss clearly makes quite a large hill of pale-coloured rock, surrounded by Torridonian Sandstone, against which the sandstone has been deposited in the manner of scree deposits.

LOCH MAREE TO LOCH TORRIDON.

Continue along the A832 towards Kinlochewe. After a mile, Torridonian Sandstone gives way to Cambrian Quartzite and Pipe Rock, overlain in some places by Fucoid Beds and Serpulite Grit, all dipping towards the east at a low angle. They form the lower slopes of Meall a'Ghiubhais around Coille na Glas-leitre. However, the summit of this hill is Torridonian Sandstone, which occurs as an outlier, thrust into this position over the underlying Cambrian rocks. Viewed from a distance, it appears as a dark mass, fringed by light-coloured rocks. Farther along the road towards Kinlochewe, the Cambrian rocks come to dip much more steeply towards the southeast, as they are increasingly affected by folding and thrusting in this direction. This is a consequence of the Caledonian earth-

69

movements associated with the Moine Thrust, which passes just to the southeast of Kinlochewe.

There is an excellent view across Loch Maree from the car-park at the foot of Meall a'Ghiubhais. The deep valley of Gleann Bianasdail makes a prominent feature to the northeast, between Slioch and Beinn a'Mhuinidh, eroded along a fault. This throws Torridonian Sandstone down to the southeast against Lewisian Gneiss to the northwest. However, the prominent escarpment southeast of this valley is Cambrian Quartzite and Pipe Rock, lying unconformably on top of Torridonian Sandstone which forms the lower slopes of Beinn a'Mhuinidh. Overlying the Cambrian rocks of this escarpment comes Lewisian Gneiss, exposed widely farther north around the summit of Beinn a'Mhuinidh. This has been thrust over the underlying Cambrian rocks, along with Torridonian Sandstone. The effects of these earth-movements can be seen just to the southeast on the slopes above Kinlochewe, where it is clear that the rocks are much disturbed.

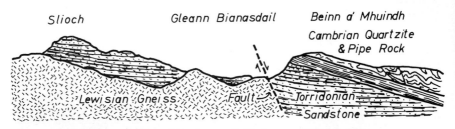

Figure 10. Slioch and Beinn a'Mhuinidh.

Turn right at Kinlochewe along the A896 towards Loch Torridon. The road follows a wide outcrop of Torridonian Sandstone, sandwiched between Cambrian Pipe Rock to the northwest and the Moine Thrust to the southeast. Near Loch Clair, the road crosses these Cambrian rocks to reach another outcrop of Torridonian Sandstone, lying well beyond the Moine Thrust. The Cambrian Quartzite and

GEOLOGICAL PANORAMA: LOCH TORRIDON

Pipe Rock can be traced from Loch Clair up the eastern slopes of Beinn Eighe, where they are much disturbed by folding and thrusting, along with the Torridonian Sandstone. The greater part of the Beinn Eighe ridge is Cambrian Quartzite and Pipe Rock, folded and thrust in a complex fashion. Only at its western end, around Sail Mhor, do these rocks revert to a horizontal attitude, unaffected by the Caledonian earth-movements.

South of the road beyond Loch Clair lies Sgurr Dubh, which consists of steeply-dipping Torridonian Sandstone and Cambrian Quartzite. Slightly farther west, Cambrian Quartzite forms a prominent line of light-coloured crags on the northwestern slopes of this mountain, surrounded by much darker Torridonian Sandstone. The lower ground below these crags is covered by a wide expanse of hummocky moraine, particularly to the southwest of Lochan an Iasgair. Continuing west into Glen Torridon, the road runs along the foot of Liathach, another mountain of Torridonian Sandstone, capped by Cambrian Quartzite on several of its peaks. The Torridonian Sandstone shows easterly dips below Stuc a'Choire Dhuibh Bhig, the most easterly of its peaks, but these rocks become flat-lying farther west, after a fault is crossed. The southern slopes of Liathach are virtually all rock beyond this point, exposing the Torridonian Sandstone splendidly in steep tiers of rocky terraces above the road.

Turn right at the foot of Glen Torridon along the minor road towards Diabaig along the northern shores of Loch Torridon. After passing Inveralligin, the road climbs over Bealach na Gaoithe, where a stop can be made at a layby [NG 827861], 200 yards uphill from the hairpin bend.

GEOLOGICAL PANORAMA: LOCH TORRIDON.

The rocks in the immediate vicinity of this viewpoint are Lewisian Gneiss, which has been faulted against the Torridonian Sandstone, exposed to the east beyond the valley of Abhainn Alligin. This steep-sided valley is eroded along the line of a fault, and there is an abrupt change in the landscape to the west, where the Lewisian Gneiss is typically exposed in a series of low rocky knolls. Looking south across Loch Torridon, the unconformity between the Torridonian Sandstone and the Lewisian Gneiss can clearly be seen on a good day. The gneiss can be recognised even at this distance, where it forms the silvery-grey outcrops along the coast. It is overlain by much darker Torridonian

Sandstone, clearly displaying its well-bedded character.
Although flat-lying, the Torridonian Sandstone rests on
top of an undulating surface of Lewisian Gneiss, burying
this ancient landscape. The Lewisian Gneiss now forms a
ridge which ends in the promontory north of Shieldaig.
Torridonian Sandstones lies immediately to the east,
where it is exposed on the slopes just behind the almost
enclosed bay of Ob Mheallaidh. Beyond this point, the
Lewisian Gneiss rises to a height of 800 feet on the
eastern slopes of Beinn Sheildaig, only to descend nearly
to sea-level once more around Balgy.

LOCH TORRIDON TO KYLE OF LOCHALSH.

Return to the main road at the head of Loch Torridon,
and turn right along the A896 towards Shieldaig. The pre-
Torridonian hill of Lewisian Gneiss can be seen at closer
quarters, just beyond Balgy. From Sheldaig, the road runs
inland along Glen Shieldaig towards the Moine Thrust,
crossing over Torridonian Sandstone. Stop just beyond the
head of this valley, where there is a fine view over the
open country to the southeast.

The lowermost slopes beyond **Strath a'Bhathaich** expose
Cambrian Quartzite and Pipe Rock, forming a slight escarpment that runs southwest towards Loch an Loin. The
flat-lying ground below this escarpment is Torridonian
Sandstone. The Durness Limestone outcrops over a wide
area above this escarpment, forming the pale-coloured
exposures on the lower slopes of Sgurr a'Gharaidh. It has
been thrust over the underlying rocks from the southeast.
Another thrust then brings forward Lewisian Gneiss on top
of the Durness Limestone. There is a very sharp contact
towards the top of Sgurr a'Gharaidh between pale limestone and the very dark gneiss on top. This marks the
line of the Kishorn Thrust, making an important feature
of the local geology as far southwest as Skye. Looking
northeast, the hills to the northwest of Strath a'Bhathaich
are Torridonian Sandstone and Cambrian Quartzite, folded
and thrust together by the Caledonian earth-movements.

Continue south along the road towards Kishorn. West of
this road, Torridonian Sandstone is magnificently exposed
in the precipices of Beinn Bhan and Sgurr a'Ghaorachain.
Exposures of Durness limestone are seen at the roadside,
south of Couldoran. These outcrops continue as far south
as Sanachan, where the road turns inland. The rocks
beyond this point are Torridonian Sandstone, lying above

the Kishorn Thrust. They have been turned upside down by the Caledonian earth-movements so that they now dip underneath the Lewisian Gneiss to the east. They can be seen dipping moderately towards the southeast as the road ascends the valley of Abhainn Gumhang a'Ghlinne towards the crags at its head, which consist of Lewisian Gneiss. The Moine Thrust is crossed on the descent towards Lochcarron, where roadcuts expose flaggy mylonites just before this village is reached.

Turn left at Lochcarron towards Achnasheen, following the A896 to the head of Loch Carron. Turn right at the road junction with the A860, and continue along the A890 through Strathcarron towards Kyle of Lochalsh. The steep hillsides southeast of Loch Carron are Lewisian Gneiss, thrust over a narrow strip of Moine Schist along the coast. Beyond Stromeferry, a detour can be made through the picturesque village of Plockton by turning right at Achmore, and following the signposts. Drive through Plockton to the viewpoint at **Rubha Mor** [NG 807342].

Looking northeast from this viewpoint, one can see a "remarkable piece of topography, without parallel in the Northwest Highlands", where the Lewisian Gneiss makes a series of bold and very conspicuous escarpments on both sides of Loch Carron. These can be traced from An Sgurr and Bad a'Chreamha in the north, through Creag Mhaol and Creag an Duilisg just across Loch Carron, to Carn a'Bhealaich Mhoir and Carn an Reidh bhric in the south. Throughout this area, the Lewisian Gneiss has been turned upside down through nearly 180 degrees so that it now rests on top of the Torridonian Sandstone, itself inverted by the very same movements.

The Torridonian Sandstone forms the lower ground to the northwest, overlooked by the Lewisian escarpment, while the contact between gneiss and sandstone dips underneath this escarpment at a shallow angle towards the southeast. The escarpment continues farther south, broken by faulting, but the Lewisian Gneiss is now thrust over the Torridonian Sandstone, itself still inverted throughout this area. This high ground runs from Letter Hill and Carn Greannach in the north, towards Auchtertyre Hill and Sgurr Mor, overlooking Loch Alsh to the south. To reach Kyle of Lochalsh from Plockton, take the back road that runs along the coast through Duirinish across the outcrop of the Torridonian Sandstone.

HIGHLAND GEOLOGY TRAIL

ISLE OF SKYE.

The trail now leaves the Moine Thrust and its ancient foreland for the Tertiary volcanic centre on the Isle of Skye. However, the Caledonian earth-movements still affect the rocks around Sleat in the southeast of the island. The Moine Thrust crosses the Sound of Sleat, giving rise to a narrow outcrop of Lewisian Gneiss along the southeastern coast of this peninsula. Beyond, there is a wide outcrop of Torridonian Sandstone to the northwest, lying on top of the Kishorn Thrust. These rocks have been carried over the Cambro-Ordovician rocks, exposed around Ord and farther north, between Broadford and Torrin.

Elsewhere, the Isle of Skye consists mostly of igneous rocks of Tertiary age, possibly erupted from the intrusive complexes of the Red Hills and the Black Cuillin. A thick sequence of basalt lavas is found over a wide area in the north of the island, forming the peninsulas of Trotternish, Waternish and Duirinish. This ground forms a lava-plateau, rising to more than 2000 feet in places, and falling away steeply towards the sea in great cliffs. The step-like breaks in this landscape, known as trap features, are an expression of the separate lava-flows which make up this sequence of volcanic rocks. Triassic and Jurassic rocks are preserved below the Tertiary lavas, in the south around Broadford and Elgol, and farther north beyond Portree.

The scenery of Skye is dominated by the igneous rocks of the Red Hills and the Black Cuillins, standing high above the basalt country to the north and the pre-Tertiary rocks to the south. These rocks are the intrusive roots of Tertiary volcanoes, now greatly reduced by erosion. The Red Hills are mostly granite, which outcrops as several distinct intrusions between Broadford and Sligachan. The Black Cuillins are mostly gabbro, quite unlike the Red Hills to their east. Together with Blaven (Bla Bheinn on the Ordnance Survey Map), these gabbroic mountains are among the most rugged in the British Isles, best explored only by experienced climbers and hill-walkers.

KYLEAKIN TO BROADFORD.

The Isle of Skye is reached by car-ferry from Kyle of Lochalsh, although a bridge may be built within the next few years. After landing at Kyleakin, follow the A850 towards Broadford, crossing at first over Torridonian

SOUTH OF BROADFORD

Sandstone for several miles. A raised beach runs along the coast at a height of 100 feet, and its deposits of sand and gravel are quarried. Jurassic rocks are then encountered on passing the road junction to Kylerhea, and these sedimentary rocks make the low ground around the straggling village of Broadford itself. They consist of a well-bedded series of limestones, sandstones and shales, rich in fossils. The lowermost beds can be studied along the coast just west of **Ob Lusa** [NG 700248], while the higher beds are reasonably well-exposed farther to the west along the northwestern shore of **Ardnish.** Low tide is needed for all these exposures.

SOUTH OF BROADFORD.

The Sleat peninsula south of Broadford lies within the Moine Thrust Belt, where it continues towards the southwest from the mainland. The Moine Thrust is seen along the southeast coast of Sleat, bringing Lewisian Gneiss forward from the southeast to rest on top of Torridonian Sandstone. Apart from the very complex geology around the Point of Sleat, other features of geological interest are seen around Ord, where Cambrian Quartzite and Durness Limestone come up from depth to outcrop at the surface, surrounded by Torridonian Sandstone. As this is the exact opposite of what would normally be expected, it is thought that the Torridonian Sandstone had been already thrust over the Cambro-Ordovician rocks by the Kishorn Thrust, before folding brought all these rocks to the surface.

Take the A851 from Skulamus near Broadford, driving south towards Armadale over the Torridonian Sandstone. Jurassic rocks outcrop west of the road, where they dip at a shallow angle towards the north, as shown by a series of dip-and-scarp features in the landscape. After reaching the shore of Loch na Dal, the road crosses the Moine Thrust at Camas nam Muilt (see OS Sheet 33), bringing Lewisian Gneiss forward on top of Torridonian Sandstone to the northwest. The gneiss makes rather bolder crags than the sandstones, even although it gives rise to more fertile ground, covered in grass rather than heather. It makes a narrow strip of land, up to 2 miles wide, overlooking the Sound of Sleat to the southeast.

Continue along the A851 towards Armadale, and turn right along the road towards Tarskavaig, south of Kilmore. This road crosses back on to Torridonian Sandstone after a short distance. Turn north on reaching the west coast at Achnaclioch, where a Tertiary dyke is exposed. Exposures of red sandstones and grey shales are seen along the road, just beyond Tokavaig, representing the Torridonian Sandstone. North of this point, the road is overlooked by Cambrian Quartzite, forming the bare slopes and rather rounded summits of Sgiath-bheinn Tokavaig, Sgiath-bheinn Crossavaig, Meall Da-bheinn, and Sgiath-bheinn an Uird. The whiteness of the quartzite appears in marked contrast with the drab nature of the Torridonian Sandstone. This quartzite ridge, rarely more than 900 feet high, is flanked to the west by Durness Limestone, which outcrops on the lower slopes just above the road. There is a fault between this limestone and the Torridonian Sandstone to the west, which is followed by the road as it approaches Ord.

The road turns inland at Ord, first crossing over outcrops of Durness Limestone for a few hundred yards before it reaches the Cambrian Quartzite. The junction between limestone and quartzite follows a slight valley, along which Fucoid Beds and Serpulite Grit are exposed in a few places, together with remnants of Pipe Rock. Where it is exposed south of Cnoc na Fuarachad, the quartzite lying to the east of this valley is steeply inclined with a north-south strike.

Just east of Cnoc na Fuarachad, a broad valley opens out to the north, marking an outcrop of Torridonian Sandstone which ends at the road. This is succeeded to the east by another ridge of quartzite, which ends to the north in Sgiath-bheinn an Uird. After passing the quarry in this quartzite, the valley of the Ord River opens out to form a wide area of Torridonian Sandstone, with a much more subdued topography. The Cambrian Quartzite continues north of the road where it is exposed in bare slopes of whitish rock, overlooking the valley to the south. The main outcrop of Torridonian Sandstone is reached beyond this point, a mile and a half from Ord. This extends east until the outcrop of the Lewisian Gneiss is encountered once more, beyond Loch Meodal. Continue east as far as the A851, turn left and return to Broadford.

BROADFORD TO LOCH SLAPIN.

Starting from Broadford, take the A881 towards Elgol. This road first crosses Jurassic and Triassic rocks, which are not well-exposed, and then a narrow outcrop of Torridonian Sandstone, before it reaches good exposures of

BROADFORD TO LOCH SLAPIN

Durness Limestone along Strath Suardal. There are good views of the Eastern Red Hills to the north, consisting of Beinn na Caillich, Beinn Dearg Mhor and Beinn Dearg Bheag. All these hills are red granite, which forms a single intrusion of Tertiary age. Their rounded summits fall away in steep slopes, covered with screes. The contact of this granite with its country-rocks to the south passes across the slopes of Beinn Dearg Bheag, above Loch Cill Chriosd. There is an abrupt change in topography as the granite screes give way downhill to much rougher ground around Coire Forsaidh. The rocks exposed on these craggy slopes are mostly agglomerates, lying within a volcanic vent.

Southeast of Strath Suardal, the Durness Limestone outcrops in typical fashion around the summit of Ben Suardal. However, the northern slopes of this hill are Torridonian Sandstone, folded around an anticline with a core of Durness Limestone. Obviously, this is exactly the opposite of what would normally be expected, but the Caledonian earth-movements have intervened, thrusting Torridonian Sandstone over Durness Limestone before these rocks were folded together to form the anticline itself. Farther southwest, the Beinn an Dubhaih Granite appears in the core of this fold, intruding the Durness Limestone. It makes the rather lower ground, covered in peat and heather, overlooking the road towards Torrin. Its contact with the Durness Limestone will be examined near Loch Cill Chriosd on the return journey.

Just before Kilbride, make a detour along a track which leads south to Camas Malag on the shores of Loch Slapin. Before reaching the coast, a quarry is seen to the west, working the Durness Limestone where it has been converted into a white marble. It is cut by several dykes of dark basic rock, which are deformed to such an extent that they have broken up into separate segments. Around **Camas Malag,** good exposures of the Beinn an Dubhaich Granite can be examined along the shore.

Walking south, the granite contact can be located within a few feet where it descends a prominent gully below the track, just before the headland at [NG 583188]. The rocks in contact with the granite are marbles, representing the Durness Limestone where it has been metamorphosed by this igneous intrusion. A feature of particular interest at this point is the presence within these marbles of dark basic rocks, forming disrupted masses, that were once basalt dykes of Tertiary age. They have been deformed as

77

a result of the earth-movements which accompanied the intrusion of the Beinn an Dubhaich Granite. They are best seen on the south face of the headland, although it must be emphasised that care is required as the rocks are very steep. Farther south along this coast, the Durness Limestone is overlain unconformably by Jurassic rocks, which make the heather-covered slopes dipping towards the sea around the mouth of Allt nan Leac.

GEOLOGICAL PANORAMA: LOCH SLAPIN.

There is an excellent view westwards across Loch Slapin from Camas Malag, with the serrated ridge of Bla Bheinn on the distant skyline. The lower ground on the far shore of this loch is occupied by Jurassic rocks, mostly sandstones and shales, which make excellent features on the terraced hillsides, descending at a low angle towards the north. They are overlain by Tertiary lavas, nearly all basalts, exposed in the steep cliffs capping the escarpments around Ben Meabost and Am Camach.

Bla Bheinn appears to the north of this escarpment. It consists of an intrusive mass of gabbro, cut by many Tertiary dykes. It is the weathering out of these dykes that gives this mountain and the other Cuillin ridges their jagged outlines, so unlike the rounded summits of the Red Hills. This difference in topography arises because there are relatively few dykes of Tertiary age cutting the granites of the the Red Hills, in contrast to their much greater abundance in the Black Cuillins.

North of Bla Bheinn, the gabbro continues to outcrop in the summits of Sgurr nan Each and Garbh-bheinn, while the next mountain to the north is Belig, which consists of Tertiary lavas, dipping towards the east. The high ground falls away beyond this point, where granite makes the rounded hills of Glas Bheinn Mhor and Beinn na Cro. This panorama ends east of Loch Slapin in the granite hills of Beinn Dearg Mhor and Beinn Dearg Bheag.

Returning to the A881, continue towards Elgol around the head of Loch Slapin. The road crosses Jurassic rocks as it runs along the eastern side of the Strathaird peninsula. These rocks are quite well-exposed along the road, while giving rise to excellent dip-and-scarp features in several places. At Kirkibost, there is a good view westwards to the higher ground formed by the Tertiary lavas, showing the layered nature of this volcanic sequence. On reaching Elgol, stop in the car-park [NG 519137] and walk down the road to the pier.

GEOLOGICAL EXCURSION: LOCH CORUISK.

During the summer months, a geological excursion can be undertaken by motor-boat from Elgol to Loch Scavaig in the heart of the Black Cuillins. The headlands guarding the entrance to this sea-loch are Torridonian Sandstone, overlain by Tertiary lavas. Beyond are found the igneous rocks which make up the intrusive complex of the Black Cuillins. These rocks consist mostly of coarse-grained gabbros, together with some ultrabasic rocks known as peridotites, rich in olivine. All these rocks are very resistant to weathering and erosion, so that they now stand high above their surroundings, forming the magnificent ridge of the Black Cuillins with its 24 peaks, each over 3000 feet in height.

Once the Black Cuillins must have been much higher, but glacial activity has been intense, carving out great corries and deep rock-basins, and leaving the ridge itself as a narrow and often sensational arete, running from peak to peak. The effects of such glacial erosion are very obvious on landing at Loch Scavaig, where the rock-bar separating Loch Coruisk from the sea has been scoured by the ice, leaving a very steep slope on its seaward side. These exposures show gabbro, which is often layered owing to varying amounts of feldspar and pyroxene in the rock. Farther afield, peridotites are exposed around An Garbh-coire, weathering to a distinctive orangey-brown.

Returning by boat from Loch Scavaig, the Island of Rhum can be seen to the south, together with the Island of Canna to its west. Rhum is another Tertiary complex like the Cuillins, while Canna is composed of Tertiary lavas. After landing at Elgol, where an excellent example of honeycomb weathering (**please do not hammer**) can be examined on the headland just north of the school, return along the A881 towards Broadford. After passing through Torrin, park at the roadside at the eastern end of Loch Cill Chriosd.

GEOLOGICAL LOCALITY: LOCH CILL CHRIOSD.

This short excursion starts where a rough path leaves the
road, 400 yards west of the ruined church at Kilchrist.
Walk 100 yards west to where a Tertiary dyke can be
examined at the roadside [NG 614203]. Up to 100 feet in
width, this vertical mass of dark igneous rock intrudes
the Durness Limestone. It makes a ridge, running southeast away from the road, covered in heather. The lower
ground on either side of this ridge is limestone, giving
rise to grassy slopes.

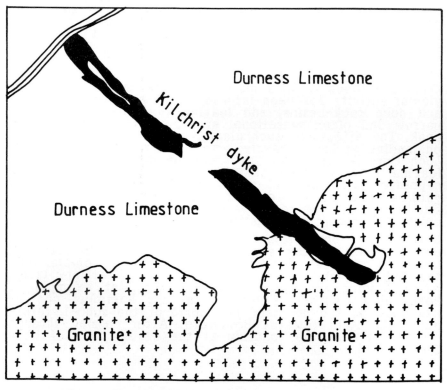

Figure 11. Geology around Loch Cill Chriosd.

GEOLOGICAL LOCALITY: LOCH CILL CHRIOSD

Climbing up from the road, a raft of limestone can be found within the dyke where a power line crosses its outcrop. Note how this rock weathers in a manner typical of limestone almost everywhere. The dyke itself can be traced as a continuous feature for 250 yards towards the southeast, until it suddenly stops. There is a break of 50 yards in its outcrop at this point, beyond which it resumes its southeasterly course. This gap in its outcrop is marked by exposures of limestone. The dyke itself continues for a short distance towards the east as a narrow intrusion of igneous rock which ends just before the fence is reached. Crossing this gap in its outcrop, the dyke can be followed for another 300 yards towards the southeast. Limestone forms a grassy hollow to its northeast, along which there are ruins of old crofts. The dyke ends just south of the last croft.

Beyond this point, granite is encountered along the outer contact of the Beinn an Dubhaich Granite. This igneous intrusion is exposed widely over the ground to the south, giving very boggy moorland covered in heather. Its contact with the limestone northeast of the dyke can be followed where heather gives way to grass. The contact between dyke and granite is less easy to establish. However, the dyke consists of dark rocks, much jointed and covered with moss and lichen, while the granite is much lighter in colour, lacks much jointing and forms rather smooth exposures. As the dyke cannot be followed into the granite, it is reasonable to suppose that the granite was intruded after the dyke, so that it now cuts across this earlier intrusion. However, following the contact of the granite shows that it forms a curious embayment along the line of the dyke itself.

Now walk northwest back along the dyke, until an old wall is reached. The granite contact follows the dyke immediately to the southwest, except that there are occasional outcrops of limestone as well. Just beyond the wall, the heathery ground underlain by granite gives way to limestone, covered in grass. The contact of the granite with the limestone can then be traced towards the southwest from this point. Tongues of granite penetrate the limestone in a very irregular manner. However, this contact becomes more regular, some 80 yards away from the dyke. Its presence is emphasised by an abrupt change in the vegetation. Note how weathering and erosion has lowered the surface of the limestone by a few feet, presumably since the end of the Last Ice Age. One consequence is that a small stream flowing over the granite descends in a waterfall as it cross the contact with the limestone, only to disappear down a sink-hole into the limestone itself.

Mineralisation has occurred in several places along this contact where the granite has reacted with the limestone. The clearest example is seen just beside an abandoned mine-shaft, filled with water, where the rock is rich in magnetite, an oxide of ferric iron. Specimens of this dark and very dense rock clearly affect a compass needle. There are also traces of bright green malachite, a copper mineral. Any mineral collecting should be restricted to some spoil heaps, which are found 25 yards northwest towards the ruins of the Old Manse. Return to the road from this point.

BROADFORD TO SLIGACHAN.

The A850 road north from Broadford skirts the Tertiary intrusions, mostly granites of various kinds, that are so well-exposed in the Red Hills of Skye. However, there is little exposure along the road before Camas na Sgianadin, where the Broadford Gabbro occurs in a cutting opposite a large layby [NG 622258]. Beyond this point, there is a thin strip of light-coloured granite, followed by altered lavas near a disused quarry at Strollamus. The road then crosses the valley of Allt Strollamus, where there is a narrow strip of Jurassic rocks, consisting of sandstones, limestones and shales, all much altered by the surrounding intrusions. Beyond this point, granite is reached just before Dunan, and the road crosses its outcrop farther around the coast towards Loch Ainort. An outlier of this granite is seen on Scalpay in contact with Torridonian Sandstone, which otherwise makes up the greater part of this island.

The road at the head of Loch Ainort then runs inland, crossing over more granite. Good exposures are seen at the roadside below Bruach nam Bo, and beyond Allt Mhic Mhoirein. Descending Gleann Torra-mhichaig towards the coast, there is much hummocky moraine, covering the lower slopes of this valley. This obscures the contact of the granites with their country-rocks, which appear as the road approaches Sconser. The view north along the coast from this point shows trap featuring where the Tertiary lavas outcrop on the hillsides above Peinchorran. Ben Tianavaig is seen in the distance as a sharp-topped hill, consisting of Tertiary lavas dipping towards the west. Its

GEOLOGICAL PANORAMA: SLIGACHAN

eastern slopes are formed by a huge land-slide, formed where the Tertiary lavas have collapsed towards the sea on the underlying Jurassic rocks.

Around Sconser, the road passes exposures of well-bedded Jurassic limestones and shales, dipping towards the north-west, before it crosses on to Tertiary lavas. These dark-looking and very blocky rocks are intensely altered in the aureole of the Glamaig Granite to the south. They can be examined in roadside exposures at the layby, just before crossing the river near Sligachan. Park near the hotel.

GEOLOGICAL PANORAMA: SLIGACHAN.

The lower ground around Sligachan [NG 48529]is blanketed with hummocky moraine, left by the glaciers when they melted at the end of the last glaciation. These deposits obscure the Tertiary lavas, which form the low ground at the mouth of Glen Sligachan as far south as Nead na h-Iolaire. However, they can be seen to the northeast, where they are exposed in the escarpment of An Leitir, overlooking Loch Sligachan to the northwest. These lavas give way at Nead na h-Iolaire to the intrusive rocks of the Cuillins Complex, which make the shapely peak of Sgurr nan Gillean, west of Glen Sligachan. These rocks are mostly gabbros, giving the landscape quite a sombre appearance wherever they are exposed. The hills east of Glen Sligachan are very different in character. They consist of steep-sided hills of light-coloured granite, much less well-exposed than the gabbros of the Black Cuillins, but covered with much scree. The dark-coloured gabbro of Bla Bheinn is visible in the distance at the far end of Glen Sligachan, beyond Marsco.

SLIGACHAN TO BERRERAIG BAY.

Take the A850 road north from Sligachan towards Portree, crossing over Tertiary lavas for the whole distance. These lavas give rise to terraced hillsides with trap featuring, as the tops of these lava-flows often consist of rubbly rock much more suceptible to weathering and erosion than their more massive centres. As the road descends Glen Varragill, the Old Man Of Storr appears in the far distance, standing proud of the lava escarpment at The Storr. As it is rarely possible to get a good view of the coast along the Sound of Raasay, north of Portree, a detour can be made along the B883 to Peinmore, where a left turn along a side road leads to Penifiler.

Parking near the end of the road, walk north over rough moorland to the slopes above **Camas Ban.** There, the view north towards Torvaig shows Tertiary lavas exposed in the headland of Ben Chracaig, and farther north in the steep cliffs that make the escarpment beyond Rubha na h-Airde Glaise. Sedimentary rocks of Jurassic age are exposed on the lower slopes below this escarpment. They are brought up to the southwest by a fault running inland from the coast, just where the escarpment ends. These rocks give the gently sloping ground that is open to cultivation around Torvaig. However, they are faulted down again just east of Ben Chracaig, where they are lost to view. Returning to the main road, drive through Portree and take the A855 north towards Staffin.

After passing through open country just north of Portree, the road comes into view of the lava escarpment which extends with hardly a break for nearly 15 miles from A'Chorra-bheinn in the south to Sgurr Mor in the north. This forms the back of a huge landslip that has affected the Tertiary lavas in the north of Skye. The landslip itself makes up the lower and often very broken ground lying at the foot of this escarpment. The Tertiary lavas forming this landslip have moved downhill towards the east, sliding on weak horizons in the underlying Jurassic rocks, as these rocks were eroded by the sea.

GEOLOGICAL LOCALITY: BERRERAIG BAY.

Driving north past Lochan Leathan, a private road leads east to the dam at the northern end of this reservoir. Crossing this dam, continue down the road to reach the flight of 640 steps which descends by the pipeline to reach the hydro-electric power station at Bearreraig Bay [NG 517527]. The coast just round the headland to the east provides an excellent section through the Jurassic rocks lying below the Tertiary lavas of the Storr. **Beware of incoming tides, and take care below high-water mark as the rocks are very slippery with seaweed.** The cliffs along this section are formed by calcareous sandstones with large concretions of carbonate, while the foreshore exposes the underlying shales, rich in fossils. These include the coiled shells of ammonites, the narrow cones of belemnites, and ordinary bivalves.

GEOLOGICAL LOCALITY: OLD MAN OF STORR

Two igneous dykes are seen close to low-water mark, where they cut across the bedding of these sedimentary rocks. The more northerly dyke shows columnar jointing and chilled margins against its country-rocks, which have been hardened by the heat of the intrusion. The other dyke has a selvedge of darker country-rock along its contacts, where the surrounding shales have been altered. Climbing back up the pipeline, the escarpment north of Berreraig Bay is seen, capped by a Tertiary sill with columnar jointing.

GEOLOGICAL LOCALITY: OLD MAN OF STORR.

Returning to the main road, there is a car-park 500 yards farther north, where a path leads up through a small plantation towards the Old Man of Storr [NG 500539]. This is an isolated pinnacle of Tertiary lava, 160 feet high and 40 feet in diameter, which stands in front of the escarpment at The Storr. It is only one of a number of rock pinnacles, isolated from one another by weathering and erosion. The escarpment itself exposes a sequence of 24 lava-flows at the very least, forming the cliff-face which reaches its highest point in The Storr. The face is also seamed by vertical gullies, weathering out along basalt dykes where they cut the volcanic sequence. The lava-flows are mostly basalt, rich in gas-bubbles. These cavities are now filled with zeolites, which are pale-coloured minerals forming hydrous alumino-silicates of sodium, potassium, calcium, barium and strontium. Good specimens can be collected from the scree slopes just beside the path, southwest of the Old Man of Storr. Blocks of bright red laterite are also present in these screes, representing the weathered tops of lava-flows.

Continue up the path from the Old Man of Storr, passing to the left of another pinnacle, known as the Needle, to its highest point, just south of a fence. The individual masses of Tertiary lava, forming the landslipped area around the Old Man of Storr, can best be appreciated by looking south from this point. To ascend The Storr, follow the path as it curves northwest into the shallow corrie northeast of the summit, which can then be reached by climbing uphill towards the southwest. **Great care should be taken as the cliff-edge is unstable.** Return back along the same route to the road.

ISLE OF SKYE

NORTH OF TROTTERNISH.

Continue north along the A855, across rolling moorland with vertical cliffs overlooking the Sound of Raasay to the east. There is a good view towards Raasay where the road crosses the steep-sided gorge of the Lealt River, showing how this river has cut down into the Tertiary sills that form the high cliffs along this part of the coast. The northern parts of Raasay are Lewisian Gneiss, giving the landscape its typical appearance, even at this distance. Farther north along the road, the dolerite forming these Tertiary sills is exposed in cuttings, just before Culnaknock is reached. Beyond this point, the fortifications of Dun Dearg and Dun Grianan are built on abrupt hills of dolerite, forming outliers of a Tertiary sill lying on top of Jurassic rocks. Stop in the car-park just north of Dun Grianan at the mouth of Loch Mealt.

This viewpoint [NG 509655] looks north to the **Kilt Rock,** so-called because the columnar jointing shown by the Tertiary sill making the cliffs at this point looks very like the pleats in a kilt. This sill is composed of dolerite, forming very dark rocks in marked contrast to the rocks which it intrudes. These Jurassic rocks are much lighter in colour, while their bedded nature is quite clear, even at a distance. The view to the south shows the sill which forms Dun Grianan and Dun Dearg at the very edge of the cliff, while another sill is present lower down the cliff. Binoculars allow one to see that this sill changes its level, cutting across the bedding of the Jurassic rocks as an intrusion, rather than a lava-flow. By walking back along the main road, the dolerite forming these intrusions can be seen at close quarters.

Continue north from Loch Mealt to Staffin, and turn left along the minor road to **The Quiraing.** This road ascends the escarpment above Loch Leum na Luirginn in a series of hairpin bends. Park where the road reaches the top of the pass [NG 440679]. Walk back east down the road to a small quarry, where the reddened top of a typical lava-flow is exposed. Farther down the road, a path leads north along a terrace to The Quiriang. All this ground is a landslip, forming great wedges of Tertiary lava, each resting on a curved surface, which flattens out towards the lower ground in the east. As these wedge-like masses slipped down these surfaces in the same direction, their upper surfaces became tilted back towards the west in a chaotic fashion. Pinnacles are formed where these tilted lava-flows have been attacked by weathering and erosion.

86

NORTH OF TROTTERNISH

Return down the road to Staffin, and turn north along the A855 towards Flodigarry, passing across the foot of the landslip. After nearly two miles, the roadside exposures around Dunans [NG 467706] show a sequence of several lava-flows, each with a reddened top (**MFG 80**), dipping towards the southeast. Just beyond this point, close to Loch Langaig, there is a good view towards the southwest, showing the landscape created by this landslip. Continue along the road towards Uig around the northern tip of Trotternish. The topographic features seen throughout this area are mostly formed by Tertiary sills, standing out as much more resistant masses in comparison with the intervening Jurassic sediments. This can be seen at Duntulm Castle [NG 410744] which stands on dolerite, while the bay just to the south is underlain by Jurassic rocks.

Continuing south, the cliffs overlooking the road along the eastern shore of Lub Score expose Tertiary dolerites with columnar jointing, from which huge blocks have fallen. Tertiary lavas then appear once more around Totscore, approximately 5 miles to the south, where they are seen in a quarry just east of the road at [NG 388661]. This is another locality showing the reddened tops of lava-flows, formed as usual by intense weathering under subaerial conditions, most likely in a tropical climate. After one more mile, the road descends to the village of Uig, where Jurassic rocks are found around the bay, faulted against the Tertiary lavas to the north. As the road climbs the escarpment to the south, good views are seen of the Tertiary lavas where they are well-exposed in the headlands of Ru Idrigill and Ru Chorachan, guarding the entrance to Uig Bay. The layered nature of these volcanic rocks is clearly visible, particularly on the cliffs to the south.

Follow the A856 towards Portree, crossing Tertiary lavas for the whole distance. The terraced nature of the hillsides, and the occasional exposure showing the reddened top of a lava-flow are characteristic features of this ground. On joining the A850, turn right at Portree and continue through Sligachan to Kyleakin, crossing by ferry taken to Kyle of Lochalsh. Alternatively, the ferry to Glenelg can be taken from Kylerhea during the summer, continuing along the trail from Kyle of Lochalsh at Shiel Bridge, or the crossing can be made by ferry to Mallaig from Armadale, rejoining the trail from Fort William at Lochailort.

HIGHLAND GEOLOGY TRAIL

KYLE OF LOCHALSH TO FORT WILLIAM.

The trail passes from Torridonian Sandstone and Lewisian Gneiss around Kyle of Lochalsh, and then crosses the Moine Thrust to reach the great spread of Moine Schists that make up the Scottish Highlands, northwest of the Great Glen Fault. These rocks are so complex that their detailed geology is well beyond the scope of this trail. Essentially, they were once sedimentary rocks, now metamorphosed to a varying degree, which appear to form two distinct sequences. The Older Moine was laid down unconformably on top of an ancient basement of Lewisian Gneiss, which now forms the intensely-deformed Lewisian inliers within the Moine outcrop. These rocks were first deformed and metamorphosed around 1000 million years ago, so that they must date back to an even earlier time. They were then affected by a second episode of deformation and metamorphism, around 750 million years ago. Only after this event were the Younger Moine deposited, possibly unconformably on top of the Older Moine, now deformed and metamorphosed as a result of the earlier earth-movements. Both the Younger Moine and its underlying basement of the Older Moine were then affected by more deformation and metamorphism as a result of the Caledonian earth-movements, ending some 400 million years ago. Only at this time was the Moine Thrust formed as a result of these movements.

KYLE OF LOCHALSH TO GLEN ROY.

Follow the A87 east from Kyle of Lochalsh towards Shiel Bridge. The route first crosses Torridonian Sandstone, overturned towards the west above the Kishorn Thrust. The outcrops along the road show greenish-grey rocks, dipping steeply towards the east, cut by many quartz-veins. These rocks have lost their reddish colour owing to the low-grade metamorphism that accompanied the Caledonian earth-movements. Farther east towards Balmacara, these rocks become very flaggy and quite flat-lying, as the Moine Thrust is approached. This carries Lewisian Gneiss westwards over the Torridonian Sandstone. The overthrust rocks are seen farther east along the road beyond Auchtertyre, where banded gneisses are exposed in a series of roadcuts. Passing through Dornie, these gneisses are very well-exposed along the A87 for nearly three miles as far as the parking place at An Leth-allt.

If stopping, care should be taken on account of fast traffic and loose rocks. More details are given in the Geologists' Association Guide to the Northwest Highlands. The main outcrop of the Moine Schists is reached around Inverinate, but these rocks are not well-exposed along the road. Continuing towards Shiel Bridge, an outlier of the Ratagan Granite is crossed, giving roadside exposures of very pink granite near Kintail Lodge.

Southeast beyond Shiel Bridge, the A87 ascends Glen Shiel, where the Moine Schists are well-exposed on the steep hillsides. These rocks are quite flaggy with steep dips towards the northwest in most places. The complex nature of the folding and deformation affecting these rocks can be seen by stopping at a large layby on the south side of the road, 8 miles beyond Shiel Bridge at [NH 027123]. Excellent exposures are reached by wading two quite substantial streams, and walking uphill over rough ground to the southwest. The second stream is the **Allt a'Choire Reidh**, which is best crossed 100 yards upstream from the bend where it changes course towards the north. Walk uphill towards the west from this point, keeping to the right of the crags that can be seen from the road, and then climb the slope to reach the top of these crags around [NH 020120]. The ridge at this point is crossed by a gully, and the best exposures lie just uphill to the southwest.

Continue along the A87 to the head of Glen Shiel, where more open country is reached, east of the watershed. The Moine Schists exposed along the road to the north of Loch Cluanie show migmatites [NH 103115] and granite veining [NH 120106], before reaching their contact with the Cluanie Granite, 4 miles beyond Cluanie Inn. There is an abrupt change in the landscape at this point, grassy slopes giving way to much more rock, eroded into smooth outcrops as the ice passed over this granite. Beinn Loinne to the south, and Carn Ghluasaid to the north, are both hills carved in typical fashion out of the Cluanie Granite. The road crosses back on to Moine country-rocks, just after the hydro-electric dam is passed at the eastern end of Loch Cluanie.

Follow the A87 where it turns right towards Invergarry at its junction with the A887, and cross the watershed into Glen Garry. Roadcuts show that the Moine Schists are flat-lying throughout much of this area. A detour can be made to **Loch Quoich** by turning right where the A87 road reaches the shores of Loch Garry, along the minor road to Tomdoun and Kinloch Hourn. After reaching the dam at the foot of Loch Quoich, continue for 1½ miles to a parking place at a bend, just below a radio mast at [NH 044018]. Walk downhill to the southeast from this point, heading for the end of a promontory, sticking out into Loch Quoich. The shore-section along the southwest side of this promontory shows several generations of folds, together with complex patterns of boudinage, all magnificently exposed. These exposures make a sloping surface polished smooth by the ice, so take care, especially in wet weather. This locality is best visited when the level of Loch Quoich is low, although this is not essential.

Return to the A87, and continue east to Invergarry. Turn right and follow the A82 along the Great Glen towards Fort William. This road follows the deep valley eroded by the ice along the line of the Great Glen Fault. Turn left at Spean Bridge along the A86 towards Roy Bridge, where another left turn should be made along the road leading to Glen Roy. After 3 miles, stop in the car-park at the viewpoint [NN 297853].

GEOLOGICAL LOCALITY: GLEN ROY.

This well-known viewpoint looks north to the Parallel Roads of Glen Roy. These are the ancient shore-lines of a lake, dammed by glaciers which lay to the south towards the end of the Last Glaciation. Although the ice had mostly melted away by 12,000 BC, the climate became much colder around 9,000 BC, when glaciers once more became established, although not so widely as before. Ice from beyond the Great Glen flowed east into the valley of the River Spean, damming the mouths of the glens to the north. This impounded the waters of a lake, filling Glen Roy and its nearby valleys to a depth of several hundred feet.

The highest shore-line lies at a height of 1150 feet (or 350 metres). This corresponds to the height of the col at the very head of Glen Roy. The lake then drained eastwards into the head-waters of the River Spey. However, as the glaciers started to retreat around 8,000 BC, they uncovered another col at a height of 1075 feet (or 325 metres). This lies to the east of Glen Roy at the head of Gleann Glas Dhoire, and the lake drained east into the valley of Feith Shiol. The middle shore-line in Glen Roy corresponds to the height of this col. Finally, the ice retreated to such an extent that the lake was able to

90

drain directly into the Spey valley across the col at the head of Glen Spean. The height of this col is 850 feet (or 260 metres), corresponding to the height of the lowest shore-line in Glen Roy.

GLEN ROY TO LOCHAILORT.

After exploring Glen Roy, return to Spean Bridge, and continue along the A82 towards Fort William. Just before entering this town, turn west along the A830 towards Mallaig. The road crosses Moine Schists lying to the west beyond the Great Glen Fault, although these rocks are poorly exposed. Beyond the head of Loch Eil, the geology becomes more complex towards **Glenfinnan,** where much granitic material is present. These rocks are best examined by parking at a layby [NM 916802], opposite a rocky bluff, covered in pine-trees. The roadcut at this point exposes granite gneiss, with thin quartzo-felspathic veins separated from one another by more micaceous rock. There are also very conspicuous veins of light-coloured pegmatite exposed all along this road.

Figure 12. The Parallel Roads of Glen Roy.

KYLE OF LOCHALSH TO FORT WILLIAM

Continuing past Glenfinnan, make another stop 3 miles to the west, where the road starts to descend sharply towards Loch Eilt near **Creag Ghobar.** Park in a layby at [NM 857816] on the south side of the road. The exposures north of the road show the complex folding which affects the Moine Schists. They can be reached most easily by walking a short distance back up the road, and then ascending a slight valley just to the left of a prominent boss of rock. This leads to a sloping shelf of rock, forming a very extensive glacial pavement. The ground drops away to the west in a steep rock-face, plucked by the ice as it flowed in the same direction across this watershed. The best exposures lie along the western edge of this glacial pavement, overlooking the glacial trough of Loch Eilt. Return to the road, and continue along the A830 past Loch Eilt. Park in a layby a few hundred yards beyond its junction with the A861 at Lochailort.

GEOLOGICAL LOCALITY: LOCHAILORT.

The roadcuts along the new section of the A830 just west of Lochailort expose Moine rocks that were once impure but finely bedded sandstones. They dip steeply towards the northwest. The second roadcut [NM 762824] from the junction with the A861 shows that the rocks on the north side of the road are cut by thin sheets of darker rock, dipping southeast at 30 degrees. By matching up the country-rocks across these intrusions, it can be seen that the overlying rocks have moved up-dip to the northwest, while the underlying rocks have shifted down-dip to the southeast. The presence of a schistosity within these thin sheets of igneous rock suggests that these movements must have occurred after their intrusion.

LOCHAILORT TO ARDNAMURCHAN.

Return to the road-junction at Lochailort and take the A861 towards Kinlochmoidart and Acharacle. The road crosses Moine Schists for virtually the whole way to Salen, cut by many Tertiary dykes. Turn right at Salen along the B8007 towards Kilchoan. Tertiary dykes also cut the Moine Schists at intervals all along this road. They are clearly seen at **Rubh' an t-Sionnach** [NM 662612], appearing as rather massive rocks with horizontal jointing, weathering to a dark brown.

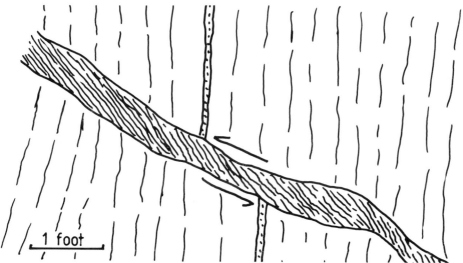

Figure 13. Schistose Dykes at Lochailort.

Once past Glenborrodale, there are views across Glenmore
Bay to the Tertiary lavas capping the summit of Beinn
Bhuidhe. After another two miles, the road crosses on to
these lavas, and the landscape changes abruptly. These
basalt lavas weather easily to a rich brown soil, giving
much more grassy slopes than the Moine Schists. Where
the road turns inland, there is a good view west to Ben
Hiant and Maclean's Nose. This hill is the site of a
volcanic vent, lying just east of the Tertiary igneous
complex, centred on Ardnamurchan itself. The ground is
poorly exposed as the road passes to the north of Ben
Hiant, eventually reaching the village of Kilchoan.

The Tertiary complex of Adrnamurchan consists of several
intrusions, mostly of gabbroic rocks, which form a series
of concentric outcrops around a volcanic centre. These
intrusions affect the topography in different ways, but
there is a particularly wide ring-dyke, known as the
Great Eucrite, which makes a ring of very prominent hills
in the centre of the peninsula. This can best be appreciated by taking the road northwest from Kilchoan, which
turns right towards Sanna after little less than a mile.
Two viewpoints can be recommended. The first is **Creag
an Airgid,** lying just east of the road, 2 miles north of
Kilchoan. The second is reached by walking half a mile
east from **Achnaha** towards rising ground, where the very

93

centre of this igneous complex is marked by a small cairn. The Great Eucrite forms a vast amphitheatre around this point, overlooking the lower ground formed by the less resistant rocks in its centre. Continue along the road towards **Sanna,** where the effects of glacial erosion are particularly clear around [NM 455690]. Similar features are seen on the slopes of Creag an Airgid.

Further exploration is beyond the scope of this trail, but the visitor is referred to the Ardnamurchan Guide, published by the Edinburgh Geological Society.

ARDNAMURCHAN TO FORT WILLIAM.

Return along the same road to Salen, and take the A861 towards Strontian and Corran Ferry, passing across the Moine Schists for the first 5 miles. Tertiary dykes are seen on the shore, just after Resipole. The contact of the Strontian Granite is then crossed near Sron na Saobhaidh, just over 2 miles before Strontian. Glaciated exposures of this granite, which carries flattened fragments of its country-rocks, are found along the shore at **Ranachan** [NM 790611], and farther east towards the head of Loch Sunart. The road continues through Glen Tarbert, which has a U-shaped profile, typical of a glacial trough. The floor of this valley is covered with hummocky moraine, while it is crossed by a terminal moraine which forms a prominent ridge of gravelly material, $2\frac{1}{2}$ miles east of the road-junction with the A884. The flat ground to its east was once the floor of a lake, dammed by this moraine. There is an alluvial fan at the watershed to the east, consisting of quite large boulders, which were dumped by the stream draining from the north.

At the eastern end of Glen Tarbert, where it reaches the shore of Loch Linnhe, the road turns northeast along the line of the Great Glen Fault. The shattered nature of the rocks affected by this fault can be seen in virtually every exposure along the road. The best view of the deep valley that forms the Great Glen to the northeast is seen just north of Corran Ferry. Raised beaches and fluvio-glacial terraces are also a common feature along this coast. In particular, there are wide terraces of gravel on both sides of Loch Linnhe at Corran Ferry, standing around 75 feet above sea-level. Several deep lochans occur behind Corran where large masses of "dead ice" melted away, leaving what are known as kettle-holes. Crossing Loch Linnhe at Corran Ferry, turn left along the A82 into Fort William.

HIGHLAND GEOLOGY TRAIL

FORT WILLIAM TO OBAN.

The trail now enters the Southwest Highlands, southeast of the Great Glen Fault. The nature of the geology is now quite different. The Southwest Highlands consist mostly of Dalradian rocks, folded and metamorphosed in a complex fashion around 600 million years ago, to judge by the latest research. They were originally a very varied sequence of sedimentary rocks, that are now quartzites, metamorphic limestones or marbles, and slates, phyllites or schists. All these Dalradian rocks were intruded by granites towards the start of Devonian times, around 400 million years ago. These great masses of igneous rock mostly form high ground, except in the case of the Moor of Rannoch Granite. The intrusion of granite at depth was accompanied by volcanic eruptions at the surface, and thick sequences of lava-flows and pyroclastic rocks accumulated on top of an eroded surface of Dalradian rocks. These Devonian rocks are now preserved in the cauldron-subsidences of Ben Nevis and Glencoe, and farther south in Lorne, resting unconformably on top of Dalradian rocks.

GEOLOGICAL EXCURSION: BEN NEVIS.

The tourist path up Ben Nevis [NN 1677131] starts from a foot-bridge which crosses the River Nevis opposite Achintee House. This can be reached from Fort Willian by turning right off the A82, just north of the town, and driving along Glen Nevis for a mile to a car-park. The weather on Ben Nevis can be treacherous, and any party should be properly equipped.

The lower slopes of Ben Nevis are formed by granite of Devonian age, which intrudes the surrounding rocks. These country-rocks are Dalradian limestones and schists, now metamorphosed by the granite into a hard, splintery rock known as a hornfels. The granite itself occurs as two separate intrusions. The outer, and earlier, granite is a coarse-grained pinkish rock, containing large crystals of felspar. This granite is cut by a dyke swarm, centred on Ben Nevis. These dykes, however, do not cut across the inner granite, so that this intrusion must be later than the outer granite. The inner granite lacks the large feldspars found in the outer granite, so that it is a finer-grained and more even-textured rock. The upper slopes of Ben Nevis are andesite lavas and agglomerates, around 2000 feet in thickness. These Devonian rocks form a plug that sank into the inner granite, probably as it was intruded upwards in a molten state.

After passing Achintee House, the tourist path first crosses over the metamorphic rocks lying in the aureole of the granite. These rocks are not well-exposed, but they can be seen in small outcrops opposite the camp-site [NN 129724]. They are pale-green rocks, rich in what are known as calc-silicate minerals, formed by the alteration of impure limestones. After crossing a stile, exposures of the outer granite are next seen along the path, cut by dykes of dark rock, belonging to the Ben Nevis swarm.

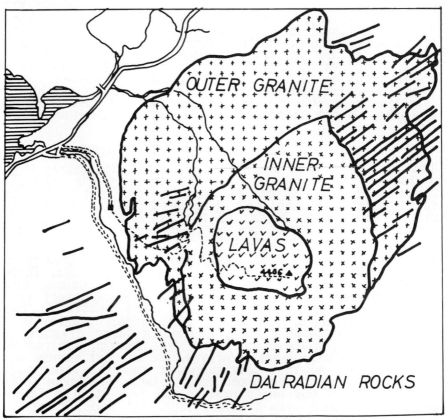

Figure 14. Geological Map of Ben Nevis.

BEN NEVIS TO GLENCOE

The granite also contains patches of much darker rock, which are altered fragments of country-rock, torn from the walls of the intrusion. There are good views up Glen Nevis beyond this point. In particular, the reddish screes on Mullach nan Coirean, another granite intrusion, make a strong contrast with the grey screes of Dalradian quartzite on Sgurr a'Mhaim.

The contact between the outer and inner granites is crossed and recrossed as the path zig-zags up the slopes south of Lochan Meall an t-Suidhe. on reaching the slopes above this lochan, the path then remains on the inner granite, which is best exposed where the path turns back towards the south. After crossing the Red Burn, the path zig-zags up the steep slopes below the summit. The volcanic rocks are first seen after the third zig-zag around a height of 3000 feet (915 metres). They continue all the way to the summit plateau, which is covered with angular fragments of andesite lava, shattered by frost.

Return down the tourist path to the car-park, and drive up Glen Nevis to **Polldubh** where the road crosses the river. Two dykes of dark igneous rock intrude the Mullach nan Coirean Granite just below this bridge, but otherwise the bed of the river is formed by granite. As they are less resistant to erosion than the granite, the river has cut its channel along these dykes, making two waterfalls where the river pours over the granite. The crags northeast of Pulldubh are another type of hornfels, formed by the thermal alteration of slaty country-rocks by the surrounding granites. They are very hard rocks, which the ice has eroded into roches mountonees with exceptionally smooth outlines. An excellent example is seen just south of the road, nearly a mile farther on, surrounded by pine trees. On reaching the upper car-park, there is a fine walk up the gorge of the River Nevis to the waterfall of An Steall.

BEN NEVIS TO GLENCOE.

Return to Fort William, and take the A82 south towards North Ballachulish. The road first follows the shore of Loch Linnhe, itself excavated by the ice along the line of the Great Glen Fault. However, just before Onich, the road turns inland towards Loch Leven, crossing on to the outcrop of the Dalradian Schists as it does so. The quartzites lying within this sequence of metamorphic rocks make prominent features in the landscape, particularly towards the east, where mountains of Dalradian quartzite rise steeply above the inner reaches of Loch Leven. The limestones, slates or schists within the Dalradian sequence give a much more subdued topography, as they are often poorly exposed. These metamorphic rocks are intruded by the Ballachulish Granite, which forms the imposing ridge of Beinn a Bheithir, south of Loch Leven.

After crossing the bridge at Ballachulish, turn left at the roundabout along the A828 towards Oban. Stop where convenient after 2 miles and descend to the shore around **Rubh' a'Bhaid Bheithe** [NN 024595], where exposures of the Ballachulish Granite can be seen. It is a rather grey igneous rock, which carries fragments of metamorphosed country-rock known as xenoliths (**MFG 95**). The granite is cut by closely-spaced but irregular sheet-joints, all dipping towards the sea at much the same angle as the slope of the land (**MFG 99**).

Return to the road, and drive southwest for 1½ miles to **Kentallen,** where cars can be parked on the old road, just before the first house [NN 010578]. The roadcut exposes a coarse-grained and very dark igneous rock known as kentallenite, rich in minerals like olivine, augite and biotite, together with some feldspar. By walking back along the road and descending to the shore where the exposures start, the contact of the kentallenite with its country-rocks of Dalradian quartzite can be located around [NN 011582]. This locality also shows an excellent example of cross-cutting intrusions of igneous rock (**MFG 90**). Along the shore to the northeast, the quartzite gives way to a typical hornfels, formed by the thermal metamorphism of a slate in the aureole of the Ballachulish Granite. It is a hard, purplish rock of rather massive texture, quite unlike its parent.

Return northeast along the A828 to rejoin the A82, and continue east along this road towards the village of Ballachulish. After crossing from the Ballachulish Granite, the road heads towards the slate quarries, where the Ballachulish Slate was once worked. These black slates are followed in their turn by the Ballachulish Limestone, which is exposed in roadcuts along the new road just east of the village. The view eastwards is dominated by the Pap of Glencoe, which is Dalradian quartzite. The A82 turns inland at the village of Glencoe. The slopes of Sgorr nam Fiannaidh to the northeast are all quartzite, while the floor of the glen, and the slopes of Meall Mor to the southwest, are mostly Ballachulish Limestone.

GEOLOGICAL PANORAMA: GLENCOE

However, once the road turns east opposite Signal Rock, it enters into the heart of what is known as the Glencoe Cauldron-Subsidence. After passing the Information Centre, turn left at the bridge where the road crosses the River Coe, and park immediately on the right at a small quarry [NN 137567].

GEOLOGICAL PANORAMA: GLENCOE.

Glencoe resembles Ben Nevis in its geological history, except that it is even more complex. The rocks forming the mountainous district around Glencoe are nearly all lava-flows and pyroclastic rocks of Devonian age, lying within an oval area, just 9 miles by 5 miles in extent. They are surrounded on all sides by a ring-fault, except where the Etive Granite has invaded the volcanic complex from the southeast. The volcanic rocks lying within this ring-fault foundered by several thousand feet into an underlying magma chamber, as its roof gave way, even while the volcanic activity continued at the surface. They are now surrounded by a discontinuous ring of granitic rock, which forced its way up the ring-fault, displaced by the volcanic rocks in much the same way as a stopper forces water out of a bottle. This granite forms the Glencoe Fault-Intrusion, and its contact with the volcanic rocks lying within the cauldron-subsidence corresponds to the line of the ring-fault.

The bridge over the River Coe provides an excellent view-point, from where many features of the local geology can be appreciated. The parking place lies almost exactly on the line of the ring-fault, and the quarry exposes the fault-intrusion, charged with angular fragments of country-rock, mostly quartzite. The ring-fault follows the prominent gully which can be traced uphill on the south side of the glen towards the top of An t'Sron. The granitic rocks of the fault-intrusion outcrop to the right of this gully. They occur in contact with their Dalradian country-rocks farther to the west. The rocks to the left of the gully lie within the cauldron-subsidence. The lower slopes mark the outcrop of the Dalradian rocks underlying the volcanic sequence itself. They are phyllites, exposed in some crags above the road, but otherwise forming rather gentle slopes, covered in grass. Uphill, the slopes become much steeper, and more rock is exposed, where these phyllites give way to the volcanic rocks of the cauldron-subsidence.

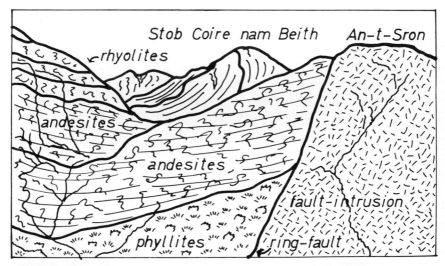

Figure 15. The Glencoe Cauldron-Subsidence.

These volcanic rocks are best exposed on the west face of Aonach Dubh (**MFG 70**), above Loch Achtriochtan. The lowermost part of the Devonian sequence consists of andesitic lava-flows, at least 17 in number, which outcrop over a vertical distance of 1500 feet on the precipitous lower slopes of this mountain. The succession of individual lava-flows within this sequence is clearly reflected in the terraced nature of the hillside. These lavas are rather dark rocks, unlike the much paler rocks which form the massive crags, capping the top of Aonach Dubh. They are formed by rhyolite, which occurs as three distinct horizons, each 150 feet thick. The two lower horizons are lava-flows, while the uppermost rhyolite is a pyroclastic rock, in which volcanic glass erupted at a very high temperature has welded together the other fragmental material. All these rhyolites are very resistant to erosion so that they form the prominent and very precipitous spurs of Aonach Dubh, Gearr Aonach and Beinn Fhada, known as the Three Sisters of Glencoe.

Traced away from Aonach Dubh, these volcanic rocks come to dip more steeply around the margins of the cauldron-subsidence. This can be seen by looking south towards Stob Coire nam Beith, where pale-coloured rhyolite dips off much darker andesite at its back, away from the ring-fault where it runs behind the summit of this mountain. Likewise, the andesite lavas forming the jagged ridge of Aonach Eagach along the north side of Glencoe dip steeply towards the south, away from the ring-fault at its back.

GLENCOE TO OBAN.

Continue east along the A82 towards the Pass of Glencoe. The lowermost slopes of Aonach Eagach are Dalradian phyllites, lying below the andesite lavas which outcrop in the steep and very rocky hillsides to the north of Glencoe. Ossian's Cave is seen high up on the face of Aonach Dubh to the south, where blocks of an igneous dyke have fallen away to leave a deep cleft. Farther on, andesite lavas are exposed in several roadcuts beyond Achtriochtan Farm. Their contact with the overlying rhyolites is seen at the roadside just before the Study is reached. The so-called "Lost Valley" lies to the south between the spurs of Gearr Aonach and Beinn Fhada, where the Allt Choire Gabhail has been blocked by a huge rock-fall from Gearr Aonach to its northwest. This valley, like several others along the south of Glencoe, follows the same southwesterly trend as the dykes which cut the volcanic rocks of the cauldron-subsidence. A stop can be made at **The Study** [NN 183562], where the rhyolite lavas show good examples of flow-folding, best seen in the crags along the old road, uphill to the north.

Continuing towards the east, Stob Gabar at the north-eastern end of Buchaille Etive Bheag is mostly rhyolite. Beyond this point, the view to the south is dominated by

FORT WILLIAM TO OBAN

Buchaille Etive Mor. The precipitous face of Stob Dearg, its most northeasterly peak, falls away from the summit in a series of vertical walls and great buttresses, seamed with deep gullies. The rock is rhyolite, and the gullies follow dykes of more basic rock, cutting through their country-rocks. Stob Dearg overlooks much lower ground at its foot, where metamorphic rocks outcrop at the surface, lying within the ring-fault. The line of this fault is crossed about a mile beyond Altnafeadh. Looking back towards the cauldron-subsidence from this point, it can be seen where the ring-fault crosses the skyline at Stob Mhic Mhartuin.

East of Kingshouse, Glencoe opens out into the Moor of Rannoch, which is underlain by granite. However, volcanic rocks are still found southeast of Glen Etive, where they are exposed around Sron na Creise and Meall a'Bhuiridh, south of the road. The road follows the slightly higher ground around the southwestern edge of the Moor of Rannoch Granite, before passing over its contact with its country-rocks, south of Loch Ba. The low ground to the east is covered with thick deposits of hummocky moraine and many lochans. West of the road lies the very mountainous district including the Blackmount, which extends without much break from Clach Leachad in the north to Ben Cruachan in the south. All these hills with only the occasional exception in the east are granite, making up the Etive Complex.

After passing Loch Tulla, where again the low ground is mantled with glacial moraine, turn right along the B8074 down Glen Orchy, just south of Bridge of Orchy. A quartz vein of exceptional size makes a very prominent feature on the skyline to the south. A stop can be made after 5 miles to view the pot-holed gorge of the River Orchy at **Eas Urchaidh** [NN 243321]. The river flows over garnet-mica-schists at this point, and thin stringers of quartzite have been disrupted by the folding (**MFG 179**). Visitors are warned against venturing on these sloping rocks, which become very slippery when wet, particularly if the river is in spate.

Continuing down Glen Orchy, turn right towards Dalmally where the B8074 meets the A85. The road first crosses low-lying Dalradian rocks around Dalmally, but the view west is dominated by Ben Cruachan and the hills to the north. They are all granite, and the geology is very clearly expressed in the topography. The road skirts the granite contact as it follows the shore of Loch Awe towards the Pass of Brander, crossing Dalradian rocks which have been thermally altered by the granite to the north. The Pass of Brander has been eroded along a fault which brought down the Lorne Lavas to the southwest by several thousand feet. These lavas are Devonian in age, consisting mostly of andesites or basalts. They are seen on the far shore of Loch Awe, exposed in the crags lying above the Pass of Brander. The road crosses the Pass of Brander Fault at the Bridge of Awe, and then continues over the Lorne Lavas as far as Oban.

In driving along the A85 from Taynuilt, stop at Connel to view the Falls of Lora. This is a tidal race which occurs as the tide flows in and out across a rock bar at the mouth of Loch Etive. It marks the lip of a rock-basin which was excavated by the ice as it moved down Loch Etive. The falls are best seen from the northern end of the bridge which carries the A828 north over Loch Etive towards Fort William. The Moss of Achnacree just beyond the bridge is a wide terrace of fluvio-glacial sands and gravels, complete with kettle-holes.

Farther west, the A85 enters Oban by descending the escarpment formed by the Lorne Lavas. These volcanic rocks are underlain by sandstones, shales and conglomerates, which also belong to the Lower Old Red Sandstone, resting unconformably on Dalradian slates. These slates are exposed at various places around the shores of Oban Bay, mostly below high-water mark.

HIGHLAND GEOLOGY TRAIL

OBAN AND KNAPDALE.

The geology around Oban is dominated by the Lorne Lavas of Devonian age, which outcrop over a wide area between the Firth of Lorne and the shores of Loch Awe. Nearly all these lavas are andesites and basalts, although there are some more acid tuffs as well. These rocks are probably the same age as the volcanic rocks of Ben Nevis and Glencoe, erupted as the granites of the Southwest Highlands reached ever higher levels within the Earth's crust at the start of Devonian times, around 400 million years ago. The Lorne Lavas, together with some underlying sediments of the Lower Old Red Sandstone, rest unconformably on top of Dalradian rocks. These metamorphic rocks date back to the very end of Precambrian times, around 600 million years ago. They make a very thick sequence of sedimentary rocks, deposited mostly as sandstones, limestones and shales under marine conditions. These sediments were then deformed and metamorphosed during what was perhaps an early phase of the Caledonian earth-movements. They are now quartzites, metamorphic limestones or marbles, and slates or schists, all affected by very intense folding.

GEOLOGICAL EXCURSION: OBAN TO GANAVAN BAY.

Follow the one-way system in Oban, turning north along the esplanade towards Ganavan. Park at the end of the esplanade near the War Memorial [NM 852309]. The coast north of this point is backed by cliffs, overlooking a rather narrow terrace of quite flat ground which lies some 25 feet above sea-level. As solid rocks are exposed along its seaward edge, this terrace is evidently a wave-cut platform of marine erosion, formed when the sea stood somewhat higher than now. The cliffs at its back are an ancient shore-line.

Walking north along the road, an old sea-stack of Lower Old Red Sandstone conglomerate can be seen standing in front of these cliffs, some 100 yards beyond the gatehouse opposite the War Memorial. The ruins of Dunollie Castle are seen a short distance to the north, standing on a bluff above this old shore-line. Although these cliffs are Lower Old Red Sandstone conglomerate, the shore exposes an outlier of the Lorne Lavas, faulted down from the east. These volcanic rocks are typical andesites, cut in some places by masses of fine-grained sediment. This has

GEOLOGICAL EXCURSION: ISLAND OF KERRERA

been washed into fissures in the tops of the lava-flows. The line of the fault can be seen at the north end of the section, where it forms a slight inlet [NM 852316].

Continuing along the road, there are several caves along the foot of the cliffs, north of Dunollie Castle. After a slight bend, the road approaches some houses at the back of Camas Ban. Just before the first house, a wave-cut notch can be seen at the back of the raised beach, some 30 yards east of the road at [NM 853317]. There are more caves cut by marine erosion into the abandoned cliff-line at the northern end of Camas Ban, where they can be reached along a path at the back of the houses.

Continue along the road to Ganavan Bay. There are good outcrops of Lower Old Red Sandstone conglomerate at the southern end of this bay, exposed on glaciated surfaces below high-water mark. Similar rocks are seen north of Ganavan Bay, exposed in the steep and quite high cliffs, which lie at the back of a narrow bench, cut by marine erosion at a height of some 25 feet along this rocky coast-line. The well-rounded boulders in these conglomerates are often very large, and consist mostly of dark-coloured andesitic or basaltic lava, together with some boulders of light-coloured quartzite and granite.

GEOLOGICAL EXCURSION: ISLAND OF KERRERA.

Kerrera is the large island, lying just offshore to the southwest of Oban. A passenger ferry runs all year round from Gallanach. The road from Oban follows a wave-cut platform along the coast, which is mostly underlain by Easdale Slates. Resting unconformably on top of these Dalradian slates are conglomerates of the Lower Old Red Sandstone, exposed in vertical cliffs at the back of the raised beach. These conglomerates are replaced to the southwest around Dun Uabairtich by andesite, making an igneous intrusion rather than a lava-flow. Just beyond the ferry, it displays columnar jointing of the most slender kind, with individual columns up to 120 feet long, curving slightly but close to the vertical.

Kerrera provides a microcosm of the local geology. The Easdale Slates form the foundations of the island, overlain unconformably by Lower Old Red Sandstone rocks. These mostly consist of thick and very coarse conglomerates at the base of the sequence, along with some sandstones and shales. They are overlain by basalt lavas, forming an out-lier of the Lorne Lavas. Several faults trend northeast-

105

southwest along the length of the island. Finally came the intrusion of basalt dykes, centred on the Tertiary igneous complex of Mull.

After crossing by ferry, first examine the rocks around the jetty, preferrably at low tide. Steely-black slates are exposed on the foreshore, just south of the pier, followed away from the sea by Lower Old Red Sandstone breccias. These rocks occur in faulted contact with one another. They are cut by a basalt dyke, weathering dark-brown, and trending towards the northwest like the other Tertiary dykes on the island.

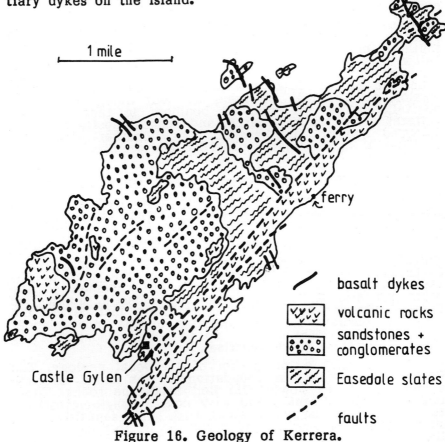

Figure 16. Geology of Kerrera.

GEOLOGICAL EXCURSION: ISLAND OF KERRERA

Walk 100 yards south across a small bay to a glaciated outcrop of Lower Old Red Sandstone lava, which lies at high-water mark. The lava is a dark rock, full of gas-bubbles, now filled with secondary minerals. There are patches of sediment occupying fissures in the lava-flow, washed in from the surface just after its eruption. It is cut by a Tertiary dyke, 18 inches across, with chilled margins.

Walk up from the shore and turn left, following the track along the Sound of Kerrera towards the south of the island. The higher ground northwest of this track is underlain by a narrow strip of Lower Old Red Sandstone lavas, separated by a fault from Easdale Slates to its southeast. These are exposed in the much lower ground along the shore, where the track often follows a raised beach, around 25 feet above sea-level. After passing Ardchoirc, a Tertiary dyke makes a wall-like feature, standing proud of the Easdale Slates that are its country-rocks, 50 yards beyond the marker for a submarine cable. Beyond Little Horseshoe Bay, the track crosses the Lower Old Red Sandstone lavas as it climbs towards Upper Gylen, only to reach more Easdale Slates. just beyond the house. These slates lie northwest of the lavas, and the contact is again a fault, trending northeast to southwest.

The Easdale Slates are exposed in places along the track as it descends towards Lower Gylen, overlain unconformably by Lower Old Red Sandstone conglomerates. At the stream just before Lower Gylen, turn left along a grassy path towards Gylen Castle. On reaching Port a'Chaisteil, continue east around the raised beach to Port a'Chroinn. The rocks on the east side of Port a'Chroinn are Lower Old Red Sandstones lavas, faulted down as a narrow strip along nearly the whole length of Kerrera. The fault separating these rocks from the conglomerates and slates to the northwest is hidden at the back of Port a'Chroinn. Just northwest of this fault is a small exposure of the Easdale Slates, overlain unconformably by the Lower Old Red Sandstone conglomerates.

These conglomerates make the low headland southwest of Gylen Castle and the cliffs on which the castle itself stands. The headland forms a raised beach cut by marine erosion across solid rock, while the cliffs at the back of this wave-cut platform once stood just above high-water mark. The caves at the foot of these cliffs were eroded by the sea, and there is also a natural arch, just below the castle. In front of these cliffs stand isolated stacks of conglomerate, rising above the level of the wave-cut platform. All these features date back to a time when the sea stood around 25 feet higher than it does today.

The conglomerates forming this wave-cut platform are cut by a Tertiary dyke, 6 feet in width, which crosses the headland just south of the abandoned sea-stacks. The sea has eroded deep gullies with vertical walls along these dykes where they reach the present coast-line.

Return to Port a'Chaisteil, where the unconformity can be located near high-water mark at the back of a small bay, just below the castle ramparts. The Easdale Slates lying below this unconformity are well-exposed below high-water mark, forming the low reefs at the back of Port a'Chaisteil. They consist of dark slates with very thin beds of fine-grained, dark-grey limestone. These limestones are tightly folded in a rather irregular fashion. These rocks are intruded by several Tertiary dykes at Port a'Chaisteil, cutting across their northeast-southwest strike almost at right angles. Some examples are very orangey-brown in colour, making a stong contrast with the rather drab limestones and slates. These dykes typically have chilled margins against their country-rocks.

Walk southwest along the far side of Port a'Chaisteil towards the very prominent stack at [NM 802264]. This stack is conglomerate, resting unconformably on the underlying Easdale Slates. There could hardly be a more perfect example of an unconformity, except that it is repeated to even better effect, some 40 yards to the west, beyond a small bay. The conglomerate is a closely-packed mass of well-rounded boulders, lying on the up-turned edges of the Easdale Slates. All these slaty rocks have a cleavage, striking northeast-southwest at a high angle, along which the rock splits with relative ease. The unconformity cuts across this cleavage, along with bedding in some places, almost at right angles.

Evidently, the earth-movements which folded and cleaved the Easdale Slates came to an end long before the overlying conglomerates were deposited. In fact, such folding and deformation must have occurred well before the prolonged uplift and erosion which so affected these rocks, that they were exposed at the surface, only to be buried once more by the conglomerate and its overlying rocks.

The conglomerates lying above this unconformity form a very pronounced overhang, running along the northwest side of the small bay already mentioned. It is possible at low tide to scramble along the narrow shelf formed by the Easdale Slates where they have been eroded away by the sea below this overhang. On reaching a slight headland at the far end of this overhang, the overlying rocks are seen to be breccias, carrying angular fragments of the underlying rocks, often reddened by weathering. They rest on a very irregular surface, cutting across the bedding of the Easdale Slates, which mostly consist of limestone rather than slate at this point. These breccias can be traced for 100 yards to the northwest, where they pass upwards into conglomerates.

Follow these conglomerates around the eastern shore of the next bay. They are cut by a Tertiary dyke, 3 feet in width, which makes a deep cleft, just south of the fence near the head of the bay. The crags stretching southwest from Lower Gylen towards the coast at this point are composed of dark sandstones, carrying much volcanic detritus, which gives them a very sombre appearance. The westerly dip shown by these sandstones brings them down to sea-level at the back of a small bay at [NM 798267], where they can be seen to overlie the conglomerates at the base of the Lower Old Red Sandstone sequence. The dark-grey sandstones are accompanied by purplish shales, which are jointed in a very regular fashion where they are exposed on the northwest side of this bay. Farther round the coast, these shales pass upwards into thin conglomerates, interbedded with sandstones.

Farther northwest along the coast, Easdale Slates make another appearance about 100 yards south of the house at Eilean Orasaig, lying in contact with the sandstones and conglomerates just to the east. They are seen again across another small bay where they are exposed on the promontory, which lies just southwest of the house. These slates are capped by Lower Old Red Sandstone breccias, and the unconformity at the base of these breccias can be traced right round this promontory to the next bay.

Walk up from the shore at this point towards the ruined house at Ardmore, passing another Tertiary dyke which stands up like a wall, 15 feet high, where the Easdale Slates forming its country-rocks have been eroded away. Continue along the path north of Ardmore, crossing Lower Old Red Sandstone conglomerates and sandstones as far as Barnabuck. These rocks pass up into basalt lavas, which form much of the very rough ground west of the path, while these lavas also occur east of the path as an outlier on Torbhain Mor. Beyond Barnabruck, Easdale Slates are encountered along the track leading back towards Ballliemore and the ferry. Tertiary dykes are seen in various places along this track, together with Lower Old Red Sandstone conglomerates, lying unconformably on top of the Easdale Slates. Just before reaching the jetty, a section along the roadside below the schoolhouse reveals basalt lava with a rubbly zone, marking the top of a lava-flow. Return by ferry to the mainland.

GEOLOGICAL EXCURSION: OBAN TO FINGAL'S CAVE.

Daily excursions from Oban visit Fingal's Cave on the island of Staffa during the summer months. Contact the Tourist Information Centre for further details. Leave Oban by boat, sailing north past Kerrera, where the unconformity between Lower Old Red Sandstone conglomerates and black Easdale Slates can be seen at Rubh'a Bhearnaig [NM 841313], together with the raised beach along the northwestern coast of this island. The boat then crosses the Firth of Lorne to the south of Lismore, where outcrops of Dalradian limestone give this island its verdant appearance. The Great Glen Fault runs between Lismore and the mainland of Morvern to the northwest.

The view north towards Morvern is dominated by the rugged terrain underlain by the Strontian Granite at the entrance to the Sound of Mull. This granite is cut off to the northwest by a large fault, running north-south, which reaches the coast at Inninmore Bay. Just beyond this bay, there is a small patch of Carboniferous rocks, overlain by Triassic and Jurassic strata. These rocks are capped by Tertiary lavas, which are exposed farther along the coast to the northwest. The boat then docks at Craignure on the island of Mull.

The coach from Crainure follows the A849 road southeast around the Tertiary igneous complex which lies in the centre of Mull. The road first crosses Triassic and Jurassic rocks in the core of the Loch Don Anticline, flanked on either side by Tertiary lavas. However, after turning inland at Loch Spelve, the road crosses the complex and very varied geology formed by the igneous intrusions and pyroclastic rocks that make up the Tertiary centre on Mull. Like all other Tertiary centres, they represent the roots of an ancient volcano, now revealed by erosion.

On reaching Loch Scridain, Tertiary lavas are again seen, and continue as far west as Bunessan. There are excellent views across this loch, showing the terraced hillsides and

110

escarpments made by these Tertiary lavas, particularly where they are exposed on the slopes of Bearraich. The Tertiary lavas end at Bunessan where the road crosses a large fault to reach the Ross of Mull Granite, and its envelope of metamorphic country-rocks, which are then exposed for about a mile to the west of Bunessan. The Ross of Mull Granite is a red and rather coarse-grained rock, exposed in smooth but rocky knolls, surrounded by peat, quite unlike the landscape formed by the Tertiary lavas east of Bunessan.

The ferry to Staffa leaves from Fionnphort on the Ross of Mull, overlooking the Sound of Iona. Fingal's Cave is the most celebrated feature of this island, penetrating 250 feet into the solid rock with its roof 70 feet above the waves. The columnar jointing of its walls occurs in a basalt lava-flow, which makes the high cliffs riddled with caves at the southern end of the island. This lava-flow rests on top of rather massive agglomerate, which is exposed just above sea-level, west of the landing stage. The columns are so straight and regular that each column can be traced upwards without any break for some 60 feet from the very base of the lava-flow. However, above this colonnade lies a jumble of smaller and much less regular columns, forming the upper parts of the lava-flow. Such columnar jointing occurred as the rock cooled down after its eruption as a lava-flow. Elsewhere around Staffa, it takes on a more convoluted form, showing how the lava cooled down in a much less regular fashion. These columnar rocks are very susceptible to erosion by the sea, as the columns fall away very easily from the rest of the rock. Fingal's Cave and several others are the result.

OBAN TO TAYVALLICH.

Take the A816 south from Oban towards Lochgilphead. The Easdale Slates are exposed at first along the road, before it reaches the outcrop of the Lorne Lavas around Soroba House, just beyond the railway bridge. These volcanic rocks are preserved over a wide area to the east of Oban, giving rise to a low plateau, rarely more than 1500 feet in height. The landscape typically consists of low knolls and steep-sided crags of rather dark rock, surrounded by boggy ground and the occasional stream. There is a northeast-southwest grain to the country, as the river valleys often follow the trend of igneous dykes, cutting in the same direction across these Devonian lavas.

OBAN AND KNAPDALE

On reaching Kilninver, a detour can be made along the B844 to **Easdale**, which is the type-locality for the Easdale Slates. These rocks are exposed along the shore at the village of Easdale, overlain unconformably by the Lorne Lavas where they form the cliffs at the back of the raised beach. The slates were once quarried at the village of Easdale, and just offshore on the Island of Easdale. They are cut by Tertiary dykes in several places.

Continuing along the A816 past Kilninver, the main road turns inland at Glen Euchar, following a well-developed terrace of sand and gravel, which can be seen on both sides of the valley. The road then follows the steep-sided valley of Glen Gallain to reach the higher ground overlooking the **Pass of Melfort.** As it descends towards Kilmelfort, the road crosses the unconformity between the Lorne Lavas and the underlying Dalradian rocks just past a small layby on the new road at [NM 846150]. The rocks lying below this unconformity are the Craignish Phyllites, which can be seen 100 yards farther south along the road, cut by a Tertiary dyke. These Dalradian rocks are more like slates than phyllites, and they show silty layers folded into an open syncline, cut across by the slaty cleavage.

The high ground south of Loch Melfort marks the outcrop of the Kilmelfort Granite, which reaches the coast around An Cnap. This granite intrudes the Craignish Phyllites. These slaty rocks give much lower ground, except where they are cut by intrusive bodies of epidiorite. This basic rock is a dolerite which was deformed and metamorphosed under relatively low temperatures at the same time as the Craignish Phyllites took on their present character. These rocks make the smooth ridges of higher ground, running northeast-southwest to form the long promontories and low islands, that are such a characteristic feature of this coast. The crags northeast of the road at Dun an Garbh-Sroine [NM 803089] provide a typical exposure of epidiorite, making a rather massive, greenish rock, never very dark in colour.

Passing the head of Loch Craignish, the view southwest shows steep slopes facing northwest, and more gentle slopes facing southeast, corresponding to the southeasterly dip of these Dalradian rocks. They lie to the northwest of the Loch Awe Syncline, which passes down Loch Awe towards Tayvallich and Knapdale. The road then ascends the steep pass of Bealach Mór, where the Craignish Phyllites give way to the Crinan Grits, lying in the centre of the

GEOLOGICAL EXCURSION: TAYVALLICH PENINSULA

Loch Awe Syncline. Continue along the road to Kilmartin, where there are several terraces of gravel at different levels along the banks of Kilmartin Burn.

Turn right a mile beyond Kilmartin along the B8025 road across the very low-lying ground of Moine Mor to reach the Crinan Canal at Bellanoch (weight limit on bridge is only 2 tons). Turn right along the B841, and then fork left along the B8025 towards Tayvallich. Although all this ground is covered in forest, the underlying grain of the country is still northeast-southwest, determining the course of the road as it wriggles its way to Tayvallch. On reaching this village, continue southwest towards Keills, but park as convenient after 1 mile where the track to Upper Fernoch leaves the road at [NR 732860].

GEOLOGICAL EXCURSION: TAYVALLICH PENINSULA.

This excursion involves a rather rough walk across the Tayvallich peninsula to its northwest coast along the Sound of Jura. There, the Tayvallich Limestone and Pillow Lavas can be examined to the southwest of Port Bealach nan Gall. Walk up the track past Upper Fernoch, and then head west across country. Stop near the spot height of 66 metres shown at [NR 723861] on the Ordnance Survey Map (Sheet 55). The ground to the northeast is underlain by the Crinan Grits, folded together with much epidiorite. These rocks form a rim of slightly higher ground, looking out over a shallow valley to the southwest. This marks the outcrop of the Tayvallich Limestone where it crosses the Tayvallich peninsula, striking north from the southeast coast at Linne Mhuirich and then southwest towards Port Bealach nan Gall on the northwest coast. The higher ground with its rocky crags of epidiorite, which lies beyond the low-lying ground to the southwest, marks the outcrop of the Tayvallich Pillow Lavas in the core of the Tayvallich Syncline.

Walk southwest from this point, following the outcrop of the Tayvallich Limestone across the lower ground towards Port Bealach nan Gall. The Crinan Grits are exposed to the northwest, forming the slightly higher ground opposite Eilean Fraoich. They are best examined on the coast just north of Port Bealach nan Gall. After crossing the marshy ground at the head of this bay, epidiorite first appears towards the southwest. It makes a low ridge of rather schistose rock forming the coast at this point. Continue southwest along the coast to reach a wall at the mouth

113

of a small burn [NR 712852]. The Tayvallich Limestone is exposed beyond this point, lying southeast of the ridge of epidiorite, which continues to make the coast-line.

The Tayvallich Limestone is a dark blue-grey, brown-weathering limestone, often sandy or even quite gritty, dipping towards the southeast. The gritty material is mostly formed by quartz grains, which are often milky-white or bluish in colour with an opalescence appearance. There are similar grains of blue quartz in the Crinan Grits. They are thought to be derived from the Lewisian Gneiss. These limestones display graded bedding where the detrital grains of quartz become finer-grained towards the top of a particular bed, away from its base. It shows that these beds are not overturned, so that the rocks become younger towards the southeast. Farther along the coast, dolomite makes an appearance in the Tayvallich Limestone, weathering to a very distinctive orangey-brown colour. These dolomites often occur as largish fragments, forming what is a breccia.

After about 500 yards, the Tayvallich Limestone runs out to sea, and the Tayvallich Pillow Lavas reach the coast near Port nan Clach Cruinn. These pillow lavas lie to the southeast of the limestone, and dip steeply in the same direction. Although they consist of epidiorite, with much the same appearance as the intrusive rock, the presence of pillows clearly indicates that these rocks were erupted as lava-flows under water. Admittedly, the pillows are not perfectly displayed, but they can be recognised by the way the outcrops weather into bulbous masses.

There are several lava-flows present along the section to the southwest. The first makes a wall of rock across the foreshore, standing 10 feet in height above the limestone and slates to its northwest. This lava-flow is typical. It has quite an irregular base where tongues of the under-lying sediment have penetrated upwards into the lava-flow, separated from one another by bulbous masses of lava. Traced along its strike towards the southwest, the base of this lava-flow appears offset every 15 yards or so, perhaps suggesting that it ploughed into soft sediment as it flowed over the sea-floor. Other lava-flows are divided by sediment into segments, or else suddenly end along strike. Commonly, the pillows are best developed towards the top of each lava-flow, so that they are most easily seen on its upper surface. The individual flows are usually about 12 feet thick, separated from one another by slates and orangey-brown dolomite.

GEOLOGICAL EXCURSION: KILMORY BAY

Return to the road by walking back towards Port Bealach nan Gall, and then following a path which climbs uphill towards the east. Leave the path where it crosses a fence and follow this fence towards Barbreack. On reaching the high ground, turn north and walk a short distance to the viewpoint, looking out over the lower ground to the northeast. This view is the exact opposite to that described on the outward walk. The crags just below this viewpoint are formed by the Tayvallich Pillow Lavas, lying in the core of the Tayvallich Syncline. The grassy outcrop of the Tayvallich Limestone can be followed around the foot of these crags, folded back on itself by this syncline. The Crinan Grits are exposed in the somewhat higher ground beyond the Tayvallich Limestone, and their outcrop can likewise be traced around this synclinal fold. There is a vivid impression of standing on the bow of a ship, facing away from the southwesterly plunge of the Tayvallich Syncline. Return southwest along the ridge to Barbreack, and then walk east across the lower ground to the road.

GEOLOGICAL EXCURSION: KILMORY BAY.

Kilmory Bay can be reached from Tayvallich by driving back along the B8025 to Barnaluasgan, and then turning right along the minor road that runs southeast of Loch Sween. After passing Castle Sween, park in the old village of Kilmory, opposite the ruined chapel. Walk back up the road to the sharp bend at [NR 702753], just west of the village. (Alternatively, walk down the path to the beach at Kilmory Bay: this avoids the need for some scrambling over rough terrain at the start of this excursion). On reaching the bend in the road, walk west of northwest along a wall to the coast at [NR 697756].

The Crinan Grits around Kilmory Bay are folded into two synclines, separated from one another by an anticline. These major folds, together with an anticline along Loch Sween and the Tayvallich Syncline even farther to the northwest, make up the Loch Awe Syncline in Knapdale. Pebbly quartzites are exposed on the coast near the end of the wall. The bedding is vertical, striking north of northeast, and graded bedding shows that these rocks become younger towards the east of southeast. The rocks are cut by a slaty cleavage along which the detrital grains in the rock are flattened (**MFG 214**). These beds can be followed for 500 yards along the strike towards the south, beyond which they come to dip steeply northeast in the hinge of a major fold. Continue along the coast over rocky outcrops, which require some scrambling, to reach the jetty at [NR 696747], opposite Eilean a'Chapuill. The pebbly quartzites pass downwards into fine-grained quartzites, impure limestones and slates, which are exposed around the low headland to the west of Kilmory Bay. These well-bedded rocks display impressive examples of quite tight folds on a small scale, all plunging steeply to the northeast. This locality can also be reached from the end of the path leading down to Kilmory Bay.

Walk southeast across Kilmory Bay. Exposed beyond some gritty quartzites are more fine-grained quartzites, impure limestones and slates, all folded together in a very spectacular fashion around [NR 700744]. It is possible at low tide to walk along one particular quartzite, following its course as it is folded back and forth across a closely-packed series of really quite tight folds. These folds plunge at a gentle angle towards the northeast, so that their crests are exposed as rounded surfaces of quartzite, rising gently to the southwest, but falling steeply away on either side, northwest and southeast.

Cross a small stream to reach more pebbly quartzites, which are exposed around [NR 699741]. These rocks dip steeply towards the northwest, while graded bedding in the more conglomeratic horizons shows that they become younger in the same direction. Around a slight headland, they come into contact with the underlying Ardrishaig Phyllites, which are well-exposed beyond a marshy inlet at Port Ban [NR 700740]. Although this formation consists predominantly of slaty rocks, these are folded together with some fine-grained quartzites in a very intricate fashion along the southeast side of Port Ban.

Walk up from the shore at Port Ban to reach the road at Fearnoch, unless planning to continue along the raised beach to the Point of Knap. Although the geology is very complex, there are many features of interest to be seen, while the Point of Knap makes a splendid viewpoint over the Sound of Jura.